# Elemental Movement: A Somatic Approach to Movement Education

## by
## Rae Johnson

ISBN: 1-58112-132-6

**DISSERTATION.COM**

USA • 2001

*Elemental Movement:*
*A Somatic Approach to Movement Education*

Copyright © 2000 Rae Johnson

Dissertation.com
USA • 2001

ISBN: 1-58112-132-6

www.Dissertation.com/library/1121326a.htm

# Elemental Movement :
## *A Somatic Approach to Movement Education*

## Rae Johnson

# Acknowledgements

The author would like to acknowledge the generosity of spirit so evident in the support and guidance offered to me by John Aram, Julia Byers, Seymour Kleinman, and Joseph Crane. Their enthusiasm for my ideas made refining them a challenge rather than a chore. My father's contribution to the process of creating this text has also been invaluable - few things are more encouraging to a writer than knowing someone you love is eagerly awaiting the next chapter. Lastly, heartfelt thanks are due to my co-researchers in the study conducted as part of this book. Their willingness to reach into the unknown to evoke experience and extract meaning was inspiring to witness.

# Table of Contents

# List of Tables and Figures

# Introduction

In a movement studio in a large Canadian city, a group of women and men are lying on the floor in a circle, arranged like the spokes of a wheel. In the center of the wheel are four objects - an earthenware bowl full of stones, a basin of water, a candle, and a feather. The faint scent of greenery hangs in the air. Over the distant mechanized drone of city traffic, the living human sounds of breath and sigh can be heard.

Almost imperceptibly at first, the group begins to move. Silently, a leg lengthens along the floor. A shoulder settles in its socket. With eyes closed and faces reflecting a quiet inner focus, the women and men perform a series of movements. Every person's movement is different, but each reflects a quality of weight, directed intent, and a clear relationship with gravity. They move as if embracing the Earth, reestablishing a connection they had somehow lost.

Then music fills the room, and the group begins to dance. The movers dance from their bones and their guts, shaping themselves into sticks and stones and bowls of Jell-O. With arms reaching and feet thumping, they create expressions of their unique and common anatomy. They follow the music's thundering rhythm and echo it, using the curves and hollows of their bodies as percussion instruments. Tracing a spiral on the ground with their steps, the movers connect hands and follow a line of linked bodies that curls and uncurls as each member of the group passes next to every other.

When the music ends, the group sits in a circle on the floor to share with each other what the moving was like. One woman shows a drawing of her feet she drew during a break. She talks about how she used to think her feet were ugly, but likes them better now she can see and feel how strong and articulate they are. A man describes how hard it was just to allow himself to lie on the floor - as if he couldn't quite trust the ground to hold him if he really let go. More than a few people are breathing from deeper in their bellies, and seem more solid than when they arrived. Before everyone gets ready to head home for the evening, they are encouraged to recognize traces of tonight's experience imbedded in their day-to-day experience.

The members of the group came to this session from very different places, literally and figuratively. Some have come from the

5

*competitive environment of the business world, and use the session to help them unravel the stress of the day. Others work in the helping professions - education, social work, or healthcare - and come here to refocus on their own personal needs and experiences, as a form of professional self-care. Still others are students of yoga, dance, or massage. Many are in the later stages of healing from various types of injury - either physical, emotional, or both - and use the sessions as part of an overall program of recovery. Despite their diversity in terms of age, culture, ability, profession, and personal experience, all share a desire to become more aware of their bodily experience, and to share that experience in a collective setting.*

*When the group meets again next week, the dance will be much different - lighter, more fluid, less direct. In the following month, they will move from five unique and distinct body/mind states, each of them inspired by a different Element - Earth, Water, Air, Fire, and Ether. Using the Elements as a framework for their explorations, they will discover new movement pathways to being grounded, flexible, inspired, passionate, and transformed. They are engaged in a process of physical, psychological, and spiritual exploration called Somatic Alchemy , and are learning one of the methods of that process - Elemental Movement .*

# What is *Somatic Alchemy* ?

# What is *Elemental Movement* ?

Although the terms Somatic Alchemy and Elemental Movement may evoke ideas and images that hint at many layers of meaning - perhaps suggesting movement, mystery, and transformation - they are used here to refer to specific concepts and methods. They were created to describe a body of work developed out of my own personal and professional explorations as a movement educator, and it is the exploration and elaboration of this particular approach that forms the basis of this text. Although the Elemental Movement session described on the preceding pages offers an illustration of this work, some working definitions of Somatic Alchemy and Elemental Movement are necessary before moving further into the text.

Somatic Alchemy is a process based on the integration of two different fields of study - somatics and alchemy. Somatics is a term coined by Thomas Hanna (1970) to refer to a group of bodywork disciplines sharing a common perspective that privileges the internal subjective experience of the body. In the West, early pioneers of these disciplines shared a concern for the discrepancy they found between the "aliveness" of felt bodily experience and the relative "deadness" of conventional approaches to exercise, dance, and physical manipulation (Johnson, 1995, p. xi). As they began to question commonly accepted notions of the body and healing, they developed approaches that included and honored what was, for them, the missing dimension of embodiment - the full experience of the self as a living body. These new ways of working with the body, begun around the turn of this century in Europe and America, included the Sensory Awareness work of Elsa Gindler and Charlotte Selver, the German Gymnastik of Mensensdieck and Kallmeyer, and the Alexander Technique of Frederick Matthias Alexander (Green, 1996). In mid-century America, influences from Eastern holistic practices furthered the evolution of somatics, and the scope of somatic practice was broadened to include Tai Chi, Aikido, and Yoga (Hanna, 1976). Today, many other schools are also widely considered somatic in orientation, such as Feldenkrais Method®, Continuum, Aston-Patterning®, Rubenfeld Synergy®, Trager®, and Body-Mind Centering®.

Alchemy - the second dimension of Somatic Alchemy - is the ancient art and science that seeks to understand the essential principles that underlie the form and function of the cosmos, and its symbols are deeply imbedded in the philosophical and religious traditions of many cultures. Alchemy is a multifaceted subject, and can be understood as a proto-chemistry, offering unique approaches to the preparation of medicinal remedies, as a source of psychological symbolism, in which the archetypal structure of human thought and feeling is illuminated, as an allegorical exploration of the journey of the human soul, and as a newly recognized influence on the world view of important writers, philosophers, and artists throughout history (MacLean, 1999). In this context, alchemy also refers more generally to the process of changing something ordinary into something special. The rationale underpinning this alchemical process dissolves traditional conceptual divisions between the contemplative and practical, as the practice of alchemy works with the physical as spiritual, and vice versa. In current terms, this process is both therapeutic and educational in nature, and involves an awareness and integration of the multiform aspects and properties of reality/experience. Thus, Somatic Alchemy is a process of transforming the *soma*, or the body as experienced from within. It is the theory and methodology in which the actual practice of Elemental Movement is grounded.

Elemental Movement is movement-centered practice based on the five Elements - Earth, Water, Air, Fire, and Ether - which are primary symbols in most alchemical traditions (MacLean, 1999). Using the Elements as a framework and as a set of symbolic tools, Elemental Movement employs movement as the primary vehicle for a wide range of personal explorations. On a physical level, the Elements provide a map for exploring different body systems and movement qualities. They are also used as instruments in the development of a high resolution body image and an expanded movement repertoire. On a psychological level, the Elements represent different aspects of the self that can be accessed and expressed through movement. Working with the

Elements as archetypes (or primal symbolic patterns of human experience), Elemental Movement echoes the psychological process of individuation through active imagination, expressed as movement (Von Franz, 1992). The improvisational movement structures also provide an outlet for creative and emotional expression. On a spiritual level, Elemental Movement serves as a form of moving meditation, drawing on the capacity of certain types of movement to transform ordinary states of consciousness into transcendent experience (Serlin, 1993). Because the Elements have been sacred icons in many religious and spiritual systems, the contemplation of them through movement can also serve a liturgical function (Starhawk, 1989; Walker, 1988).

The rationale that underlies the practice of Elemental Movement is both simple and multifaceted. The basic premise is somatic in its perspective, and proposes that human functioning and experience is enriched through enhanced self-awareness[1]. In turn, increased awareness promotes freedom of behavior through an increase in the range of choices available to us in response to inner needs and the demands of our environment (Green, 1996). Therefore, the fundamental objective of Somatic Alchemy as expressed through Elemental Movement is an increased ability to use oneself fully - to respond effectively, fluidly, and with pleasure to the challenges of being alive.

The first section of this book will offer a deeper look at Somatic Alchemy , with an emphasis on describing its historical and theoretical underpinnings. In laying the foundation for this

---

[1] Somatic movement therapy and education, as defined by the International Somatic Movement Education and Therapy Association (ISMETA), is a movement-centered approach that utilizes a range of techniques to help clients and students recognize and improve psycho-physical and cognitive-motor movement patterns and stress-related emotional conditions. These techniques include physiological repatterning to enhance awareness and usage of various body systems (i.e. perceptual, muscular, skeletal, neurological, etc.), movement analysis to optimize one's movement potential through exploration of various movement patterns and qualities, and facilitating psychological and emotional expression through exploring the non-verbal dimensions of human interaction in terms of emotional and psychological attitudes and relationships.

exploration, it is important to acknowledge that this work has its roots in many fields, and most of them will only be cultivated here in a very specific context. The primary focus throughout is how a particular set of symbols - the Elements - are used as the medium and instruments in changing internal felt perception. The resource section at the end of the book offers some suggestions to those wishing to pursue further research into the areas of somatics, alchemy, or movement therapy.

The second section focuses on the practice of Elemental Movement itself. Divided into five main chapters - one for each of the Elements - it includes an explanation of the overall structure of an Elemental Movement session as well as offering detailed movement experiments for each Element. These experiential sections are prefaced by relevant background material designed to elaborate on the themes embodied by the movement structures, and to offer a broader context in which to understand them. Some of the topics woven into these chapters include experiential anatomy, contemplative movement, breathwork, sensory awareness, and authentic movement.

Before moving into the main text, however, some mention of the personal dimensions of the development of Somatic Alchemy and Elemental Movement is in order. The process of engaging in this work can be a deeply personal one, and I thought it important that the reader be able to connect a description of it to some sense of the real person who conceived it. To that end, I offer here a brief history of the heuristic inquiry that led to this manuscript. I also believe in articulating my personal biases when offering ideas up for consideration, especially when suggesting those ideas be explored experientially, as I am in this manuscript. The perspectives I work from are named and described here initially, so that they may be more easily recognizable as they appear in context later on.

I have used movement as my primary medium of personal expression, therapeutic exploration, and spiritual practice for as long as I can remember. As a child, I danced my imagination and let movement reveal emotions I had no words for - stomping and sweeping and whirling as a way of understanding and expressing myself. In addition to the personal expression it offered, movement also conferred the rare and precious gift of transcendent experience. Despite my youthful inexperience with life's spiritual dimension, I understood in my bones that the sacred was, for me, a bodily experience. Movement was the medium that confirmed my connection to something universal while simultaneously validating my authentic personal identity. Wordlessly, these mysterious and deeply inspiring experiences reminded me who I was, and why I was alive. I began to seek them out, and to find out how to recreate them instead of simply waiting and hoping for them to happen.

Over the years, I explored what I believed were the underlying components of these experiences, studying psychology, philosophy, spirituality, and the movement arts. My clinical work as a therapist and as a movement educator lent weight and depth to my understanding, but I was still searching for a reliable method for eliciting transcendence through movement. My explorations led me to investigate the pagan spiritual practices of my ancestors, and I discovered that, like alchemists, my forebears understood my transcendent experiences as *ethereal* in a very different sense of the word than I did. They saw the ethereal not as something that appeared magically out of thin air, but very practically as something that was made up of four basic Elements. Ether, or ethereal experience, could be created through unifying these Elements.

If Ether emerges as a result of the balanced integration of Earth, Water, Air, and Fire, then the ethereal movement experiences I sought should be generated by embodying these Elements in a balanced way. My knowledge of somatic psychology suggested that we *do* embody the aspects of our environment that are significant to us, and an almost universal ancient philosophy asserted that our bodies were already composed of these basic Elements anyway, although not necessarily in equilibrium. With these thoughts in mind, I began to formulate the following questions - How do we embody the Elements? Does the balanced and integrated embodiment of the Elements facilitate Ethereal experience? Using the tools of exploration acquired through my training in psychotherapy and movement education, I began to play with the Elements through movement. Over the years, Somatic Alchemy   and Elemental

Movement    grew out of these explorations. As these ideas and practices developed, they evolved into something that, for me, transcended the initial impetus.

As an approach to somatic education, Somatic Alchemy and Elemental Movement    reflect a synthesis of dozens of approaches to therapy, personal growth, and movement education I have encountered and assimilated over the past several decades. Despite these myriad influences, however, there is a single essential thread that runs through this work, and informs every exercise and explanation contained within it. This fundamental premise - one that I call a *feminist somatic* perspective - sees the body and our relationship to it as key to personal and social transformation (Johnson, 1996). Feminism has been instrumental in recognizing the deep imprint left by all forms of violence and oppression. In her book Trauma and Recovery (1992), Judith Lewis Herman makes critical connections between different forms of violence, and draws parallels between the private violence experienced in the lives of women and children, and the public violence of war and terrorism. She asserts that there are important relationships between our personal experiences and the political context in which they occur, and that the legacy of various forms of trauma touches every facet of our society.

Somatic theorists suggest that this legacy is perhaps most strongly felt in our bodies, and the massive global incidence of war, politically directed torture, famine, rape, and domestic violence in this century indicates a "...criminal disregard for the muscle fibers, fluids, and neural networks in which we live" (Johnson, 1995, p.ix). In that respect, this work is offered as a tool for healing and reclaiming our bodies for ourselves, and understands this process as both a personal and political act. My feminist somatic bias also has important implications for how I present this material - my intent is to offer something that can be used by others to create for themselves the changes they would like to make in their bodies and their lives. This text is a map for guided self-exploration, not a manual for effecting predetermined ideals, and designed more as inspiration than instruction.

In that spirit, it is possible to trace some of the lines on this map back to their places of origin, and discover that the central concepts at work in Somatic Alchemy and Elemental Movement are actually very old. Both the idea that personal and collective transformation can be effected through movement, and that the Elements can serve as symbols of microcosmic and macrocosmic change are rooted in ancient beliefs and practices (Serlin, 1993; Walker, 1986; Godagama, 1997). This section begins by tracing the Elements over time, between cultures, and through the often intersecting fields of alchemy and psychology.

# Ancient Alchemy: The Elements Through the Ages

The Elements have served as essential cosmic principles and as tools of transformation for many thousands of years in the ancient civilizations of China, India, and Greece. Each developed unique ways of working with the Elements in order to effect and understand change. These Elementary ideas and explorations can be found in the foundations of the philosophy, chemistry, and medicine of these cultures. Originally, these disciplines were not separate and distinct fields of study, but were embraced by a single multifaceted pursuit called alchemy (MacLean, 1999). Stated simply, alchemy is the study of the nature and working of the universe, and early alchemists were the philosophers, healers, and scientists of their day. Because this search for the keys to universal change possessed both tangible and abstract dimensions, alchemical practice reflects these two different streams of emphasis. One of the most common misperceptions about alchemy is that it is exclusively concerned with the mundane objective of turning base metals into gold. Although practical alchemists did pursue this goal for thousands of years, and in so doing invented much of the laboratory apparatus and procedures still in modified use today, internal alchemists pursued knowledge of the cosmos through a deeper understanding of the workings of the human body, mind, and spirit.

The alchemical and philosophical schools of these early cultures devised many types of symbols in the course of their investigations, but the Elements are the symbols that form the heart of their cosmologies (MacLean, 1999; Godagama, 1997; Walker, 1986). In each culture, these universal building blocks have evolved differently. In China, they are fundamental to the ancient text of the I Ching[2] (Walker, 1986), but a slightly different

---

[2] The *I Ching* (pronounced Yee-Jing) is an ancient Chinese text comprised of philosophical, astrological, and symbolical writings. One of the four pillars of Taoism, it uses 64 hexagrams, or symbolic representations of human experience, to illustrate the laws of universal change (Chang, 1978).

set of Elements is employed in Chinese alchemy and medicine (Pregadio, 1999). In India, the Elements are central to the practice of Ayurvedic medicine, and remain an active conceptual component of modern health care in that country. In the West, the Elements have undergone various developments in the hands of Greek philosophers, Sufi poets, and medieval alchemists. Sometimes the Elements are seen, as did Aristotle, as actual physical substances. Other times, as with Chinese alchemy, they are viewed more as metaphysical forces (Conder, 1999). Despite these shifts in usage, emphasis, and conceptualization, the Elements have retained an essential character that is recognizable from one culture and era to the next. It is this underlying essence that I hope to draw out and make visible as we travel into the history of the Elements.

# The Chinese Elements

## Elemental Children.

In the beginning, there was Chaos. Like the creation myths of ancient Egypt, Greece, Persia, and India, the Chinese story of the Elements begins here, with the primal soup. Essentially matrifocal in perspective, this prehistoric mythos conceives of the beginning of the world as a process of birth, and of all things as children of a primordial Mother. Whether known as Kali-Maya (in India), Temu (in Egypt), Tiamat (in Babylon), or Nu-Kua (in China), this cosmic Mother was initially without form or boundary. Conceived of as a dark semi-liquid mass of undifferentiated potential matter and energy, this Original Source began to dance, and through her rhythmic movement generated the energy to coagulate the homogeneous expanse of the universe into separate, differentiated, and ordered components (Walker, 1986, pp. 1-6).

To the prehistoric Chinese, the first "children" born of the Great Mother were the Elements, and formed a cosmic family - mother Earth and father Sky, with their children Water, Sea, Fire, Thunder, Breath, and Mountain (Legge, 1964, p.350; Walker, 1986, p.5; Wing, 1982, p. 15). In this family, each of the four primary

15

Elements in its purest essence is paired with a representation of itself as expressed and experienced on a earthly level. In this way, a symbol set is developed that includes both the transcendent Elemental spirit as well as its more mundane form. Breath is the intermediary of Father Heaven or Air, Mountain the material form of Mother Earth, Fire is manifested as Thunder, and Sea is Water's expression on a more human scale (Walker, 1986, p.5). The concept of the Elements as children and as inextricably related to one another as are members of the same family stems from this early stage in the development of Chinese metaphysics, and endures in many current systems.

## Elements as Polarities.

Considered one of the oldest established schools of Chinese religious and philosophical thought, Taoism represents an abstraction and elaboration on the anthropomorphic depiction of the cosmos in earlier myth. Here, the universe is conceived of as the final stage in a series of spontaneous transformations from an originally unified Void. According to Neo-Confucian scholar Chu Hsi (c.1200),

> In the beginning, before any being existed, there was only Li, then when it moved it generated the Yang and when it rested it generated the Yin. Upon reaching the extremest point of rest it began to move once more, and at the extremest point of motion it began to return to rest once more..

(Bender, 1997, p. 1)

These movements generated the separation of the Tao into the two complementary, dynamically interacting polarities called Yin and Yang - expansion and contraction, inhalation and exhalation, light and dark, active and receptive, male and female. This process of separation and transformation of matter began an eternal cycle of "becoming" that governs all life. The cycle of Yin and Yang is depicted in the classic Taoist symbol that shows them endlessly pouring into each other while containing the seed of their antithesis in their deepest core. Yin and Yang both create and destroy one another, and this paradoxical cycle of change is at the heart of Taoist belief.

According to Taoist theory, Yin and Yang combine to produce the four Hsiang (or Diagrams), which in turn produce eight Pa Kua (or Trigrams). This evolving differentiation of the cosmos is simpler to conceptualize when represented graphically - Yin is denoted by a broken straight line, indicating its receptive nature; a solid line represents Yang. The four Diagrams are all the possible combinations of Ying and Yang in a two-line arrangement, and the Trigrams all the possible combinations of Yin and Yang in a three-line arrangement. The Eight Elemental Trigrams are arranged using the same simple but elegantly logical binary system used by modern computers.

When each of these basic units is paired with every other unit in an grouping that arranges one trigram directly above the other (as a six-lined figure, or hexagram), all the possible combinations and arrangements of these eight trigrams become the 64 hexagrams found in the I Ching, the ancient Chinese Book of Changes. The "changes" refer to the continual process of transformation of the Elements that continue to be generated by the rhythms of the dancing universe. By observing these cosmic rhythms as manifested in the changing seasons, tides, and cycles of birth and death, the Chinese were able to identify the universal principles that govern change, and classify everything in the universe in terms of its composite nature. A table of correspondences for the Pa Kua is offered below to indicate the complex layering of meaning inherent in the system. Far from being arbitrary assignments of meaning, these correspondences were carefully developed through an analysis of the composition of each Pa Kua in terms of their essential Yin/Yang qualities.

# Table of Correspondences of the Elements in the I Ching

| Name | Element | Relations | Qualities | Body Part | Season | Direction |
|------|---------|-----------|-----------|-----------|--------|-----------|
| Ch'ien | Heaven | father | creative strong light firmness | head | early winter | northwest |
| Chen | Thunder | eldest son | expansion activity excitement growth | foot | spring | east |
| K'an | Water Rain | middle son | danger profound mystery depth | ear | mid winter | north |
| Ken | Mountain | youngest son | stillness calm stubborn tranquil | hand | late winter | northeast |
| K'un | Earth | mother | yielding dark receptive nourishing | belly | early autumn | southwest |
| Sun | Wind | eldest daughter | gentle simple honest penetrating | thigh | early summer | southeast |
| Li | Fire | middle daughter | clarity intelligence consciousness illuminating | eye | mid summer | south |
| Tui | Lake | youngest daughter | openness satisfaction fullness pleasure | mouth | late autumn | west |

*Chart adapted from Wing, 1982, p.15*

# The Alchemical Microcosm.

The primary source of Chinese alchemical knowledge is the Taoist texts, and the alchemical tradition in China is based on the concepts of Tao and Yin/Yang (Pregadio, 1999). During the early Han dynasty (207 BCE - 9 AD), philosophers attempted to synthesize the many ideologies developed in China over the previous three hundred years, and attempted to derive from the classic texts a unified principle of the workings of the universe. Appended to the I Ching, this new theory was the origin of the Five Agents Wu Hsing school (Hooker, 1996) employed by Chinese alchemy (Pregadio, 1999). Although the Five Agents (or Five Element) theory employs a different set of elements than described in the I Ching (wood, metal, fire, water, earth), the process of integration and transformation reflects the same basic underlying principles of universal change.

The fundamental task of Chinese alchemy is to retrace the process of the creation of the universe backwards - by reuniting the elements of the cosmos into its essence, the Tao (Pregadio, 1995-96). The exploration of the underlying principles of the form and function of the cosmos may be pursued externally, through the practical manipulation of natural substances and compounding of elixirs (known as *waidan*), or internally, through a tradition called *neidan*. Developed as an independent discipline around the beginning of the Tang period, *neidan* views the human body as a microcosm of the larger universe, and seeks to understand the workings and movements of the Tao as they manifest within us. In internal alchemy, the language of the laboratory was applied to the operations realized inside the body (Pregadio, 1999). Although these procedures are described very elusively in the ancient texts, lead is often used as a cover name to describe pure Yang, or knowledge of the Tao. On the other hand, mercury is used to represent the individual mind. Through a process of repeated cyclical procedures carried out in movement and meditation, Yin and Yang are reunited and the final object of internal alchemy is attained - an elixir called *huandan*, or the elixir of return.

In the spirit of the *neidan* school of internal alchemy, the following poem suggests some of the implications in viewing the human body as a microcosm of the larger universe.

*earth mother inside / inside mother earth*

*i am reclaiming my body land*
*cells like drops of rain on open fields*
*sinking in and drinking deeply of the knowledge in my bones*
*i am putting my hands on the planet*
*i am lying full length face down into the earth*
*and we are revolving in space together*
*through me and throughout me*
*the mother reconnects us*
*this arm...that hill...this ankle*
*the wide curve of water and stone that is the belly of the sea*
*when i roll over to face the sky*
*the depth of it sends me reeling*
*i catch my breath*
*inhaling sky...exhaling me*
*the mother weaves the world and i together*
*in the light of day she illuminates me*
*in the dark of night she links constellations within my skin*
*we both have stars in our eyes as*
*she tells me with her body*
*and i tell her with mine*
*if this is the universe*
*we must be home*

# India and the Ayurvedic Elements

Ancient Hindu sacred scriptures, the Vedas, contain the many of the same references to alchemy found in Chinese texts. Similarly, pre-Vedic Tantric mythology views the birth of the cosmos as a function of the Great Mother, with Kali as an ocean of blood giving birth to the Elements as Sanskrit letters (Walker, 1986; Walker, 1988). The sounds of these Elemental letters - *La* (Earth), *Va* (Water), *Ya* (Air) and *Ra* (Fire) - formed the first mantras and brought the universe into existence. The earliest records of Indian natural philosophy, dating from the 5th century BCE, also refer to the Elements, as well as to the concept of polarized forces or energy. As with the Chinese perspective, these polarized forces are seen as complementary rather than antagonistic, and constantly in the process of change and transformation.

## The Healing Elements.

Much of the alchemical experimentation conducted in ancient India centered on the Elements as medicine, and as a way to understand the workings of the human body. The tradition of Ayurvedic medicine that developed from these experiments is several thousands of years old, and continues to be a favored form of health care in India and large parts of the Eastern world (Godagama, 1997).

According to Ayurvedic theory, the body is composed of and governed by the Elements (Godagama, 1997). Earth is the body's flesh and bone, and Water its blood and fluids. Fire affects hunger, thirst, and sleep, Air influences bodily motion, and Ether[3] governs the interspaces of the stomach, heart, and neck. The five senses of the human body also correspond to the Elements - sound is transmitted through Ether, Air influences the sense of touch, Fire allows the perception of sight, Water affects the perception of

---

[3] Ether is the "Element that is not an Element". Rather, it is the elusive quintessence that includes, integrates, and transcends the other four Elements.

taste, and Earth is connected to the sense of smell. In this way an Elemental anatomy and physiology is established.

## The Constitutional Elements.

Ayurvedic theory works with the Elements in three basic combinations, and are considered to embody the fundamental principles of the constitution of the human being. Ayurveda teaches that these constitutional types - or *doshas* - combine two of the five Elements: *Vata* is Ether and Air, *Pitta* is Fire and Water, and *Kapha* is Water and Earth. Each individual (indeed, everything in the world) possesses a unique combination of these Elementally-based bio-energies in which one is predominant (Godagama, 1997). One's *dosha* is determined before birth at the moment of conception, and many factors come into play influencing it - including genetic inheritance, astrological conditions, and *karma*. An Ayurvedic practitioner is trained to evaluate one's *dosha* by assessing a wide range of factors, including height, weight, facial features, circulation and pulse rate, sleep and dream patterns, memory and thought patterns, tendency toward types of illness, appetite and preferences for food and drink, and levels of physical activity.

*Vata* energy, composed of Air and Ether, is considered one of the most influential *doshas*, guiding all bodily functions and body movement. *Vata* also corresponds to the nervous system, and could be said to be equivalent to the modern concept of neurotransmitter activity in the brain. It is dry, light, rough, and quick, and *Vata* types tend to be slim, athletic, ethereal, and creative. *Pitta* types, in contrast, are more stable and substantial, with a tendency toward ambitiousness and an appreciation for the good life. As *Pitta* governs the generation and conservation of body heat, digestion, metabolism, those with a predominantly *Pitta* constitution often perspire heavily and tend toward a high body temperature and a strong metabolism. *Kapha*-dominant people tend to be slower, more conservative, and generally less active than the other doshas. Governing the Earthy qualities of strength and mass, *Kapha* also regulates the water functions of the body and maintains the immune system (Godagama, 1997).

The Elements also act as links between the external world and the internal world of the body. Thus, the external Air corresponds to the internal Vata, the external Fire to Pitta, and the external Water to internal Kapha. Any change in the Elementary condition of the external world is thought to influence corresponding changes in the internal human body. For example, high levels of Pitta (predominantly Fire) in the body would be soothed and balanced by the presence of Kapha (predominantly Water) in the external environment. In a recent consultation with an Ayurvedic practitioner, my predilection for damp weather was considered an indicator of my basic Pitta constitution.

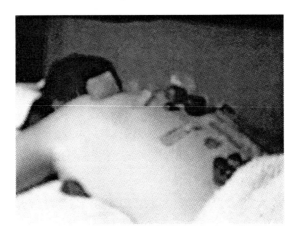

*Chakra balancing with gemstones as part of an Ayurvedic bodywork treatment*

Enhancing *dosha* balance is one of the central aims of Ayurvedic medicine. Ayurvedic medicine employs a variety of methods, including herbal preparations, yoga, and dietary recommendations. My own personal consultation in Ayurvedic bodywork included aromatherapy massage with essential oils, crushed dried herbs applied externally to the skin and inhaled through a steam tent, gemstone crystals placed on the *chakra* energy centers along the spine, and a treatment called *shirodhara* in which a continuous stream of warm liquid was directed to a point between the eyebrows. Because of my diagnosed tendencies toward a mainly fiery constitution, the treatment was directed toward soothing and cooling preparations. Vata (Airy) types would receive treatments designed to calm and ground, and the focus in a Kapha (Watery) treatment would include preparations and procedures designed to stimulate and purify. Thus, the emphasis on balancing one Element with the others through their complementary action is realized.

*Inside an Ayurvedic treatment center*

# The Western Way

Tracing the Elements along their Western path involves a discussion of some of the developments made by Greek philosophers and European alchemists over the span of several thousand years. Because of the significance of Greek philosophy to modern approaches to thought and perception, early Greek conceptions of the Elements will be described, as well as how they formed the basis of later developments in alchemy and medicine. As with their Chinese and Indian counterparts, Greek philosophers used the Elements as conceptual building blocks, and used them to describe the qualities and properties of the world they knew.

## The Natural Elements.

Greek Elemental theory can be divided into two main periods - Monism and Pluralism. These early philosophers were the first Greeks to postulate purely natural, rather than mythological, explanations for the origin of the universe. The Monists believed that the universe was based on a single Element. Considered the first Greek philosopher, Thales of Miletus (c. 615 BCE) contended that Water is the source of all things (Cohen, 1997). His successor, Anaximander, postulated a more abstract account of the origin of the cosmos. He asserted that everything evolved out of the *apeiron*, which itself possessed no distinguishable qualities, but was the limitless source from which all things came to be and to which they eventually returned. Anaximander's student, Anaximenes, believed that the universe was created from Air (or *Aer*), developing through a process of condensation and rarefaction. Although Aer was invisible to the sight, it was revealed by cold, heat, moisture, and especially movement. Constantly in motion, Aer's condensing and expanding (rarefying) movements generated all things. When Aer became rarefied it formed Fire, and when condensed it became clouds and eventually Water. Condensed further still, it formed Earth, and finally stone (Cohen, 1997). The last of the Monists, Heraclitus of Ephesus, was said to have chosen Fire as the primary

Element as it best exemplified the violent change inherent in the cosmos (Pineault, 1997).

Empedocles of Agrigentum (500-435 BCE) was first to propose that the cosmos was based on four Elemental properties, and that everything contained the qualities of all four of the Elements in varying quantities. Thus, a tree possessed more Earth than a jellyfish, but less than a stone. Empedocles envisioned the Elements as swirling out of a single cosmic vortex and establishing what is now considered the traditional Western ordering of the Elements - Earth, Water, Air, and Fire. Because Fire was the lightest and most refined of the Elements it flew furthest and highest. Air was next lightest and second highest, followed by Water, and ending with Earth, the heaviest of the Elements (Pineault, 1997). As a medical practitioner as well as a philosopher, Empedocles was also important in the evolution of Greek medicine (Demand, 1997).

The Elements also form part of Plato's cosmology, as evidenced in his writing. In the *Timaeus,* Plato asserts that the physical world was created by a *demiurge*, or creator, who imposed form on originally formless material (Cohen, 1997). He offers detailed geometrical descriptions of the four Elements (Earth, Water, Air, and Fire), and integrates the ideas of Pythagoras, Democritus, and Empedocles in his Elemental theory. Each Element was made up of a different kind of particle, which were in turn composed of right triangles. Fire was a tetrahedron, or four-sided solid. Air was an (eight-sided) octahedron, Water a (twenty-sided) icosahedron, and Earth a cube.

These early developments in Western Elemental theory formed the basis for later advances in medical and alchemical knowledge. With each successive development and new application, the Elements become more multifaceted, gaining depth and richness as symbols.

## The Temperamental Elements.

Hippocrates, long considered the father of Western medicine, developed a physiological doctrine based on the Elements in the fifth century BCE. This theory formed the basis of most Hippocratic medicine, and was interpreted in terms of Empedocle's four Elements (Demand, 1997). According to this theory, the human body is composed of four basic fluids or *humors* - blood, phlegm, yellow bile, and black bile - which are in continuous circulation throughout the body (Marketos, 1997). Each of these humors was based on the Elements and possessed specific qualities related to them. The internal balance of these four fluids was an indicator of physical health, and sickness was considered to arise out of their disequilibrium.

Several hundred years later, Galen developed this humoral theory further, and began to make direct causal connections between bodily constitution and psychological character. A preponderance of blood indicated a sanguine or Airy temperament, excess phlegm denoted a phlegmatic disposition ruled by Water, the Fiery choleric temperament involved excess yellow bile, and too much Earth-based black bile caused a melancholic temperament. The four Elemental humors served as the basis for medicine and medical psychology throughout the Middle Ages and continued as fundamental concepts for many centuries (Demand, 1997).

## The Elements and the Western Alchemists.

The roots of Western alchemy are visible in the metallurgic and chemical practices of ancient Egypt, where they spread from there to Greece and Rome. The golden age of practical, or external, alchemy in the West occurred in the 3rd century AD with the development of an alchemical academy founded by Zozamus of Penopolus, who first postulated the existence of the philosopher's stone, a classic alchemical symbolic device. The 8th century saw important translations of classic alchemical works into Arabic, and it is from this language that the word *alchemy* is derived, meaning the art of metallurgy. The

Jewish Quabballah also contains alchemical imagery and symbolism, and translations of the Mishneh Torah refer specifically to the four Elements as the basic building blocks of the universe (O'Levy, 1993). Although this early period saw the flowering and sowing of alchemical ideas into many cultures, it is not until the Middle Ages that alchemy in the West begins to orient itself to the internal realm of the body.

The famous Swiss physician Paracelsus (c. 1500) was figural in shifting the emphasis from the external alchemy of metallurgy and chemistry to the personal alchemy of healing. Using alchemical concepts and procedures, he was the first to accurately diagnose syphilis and treat epilepsy as a disease (rather than as possession by evil spirits), and is also credited with discovering the opiate derivative *laudanum*. Central to Paracelsan thought is the respect for one's own experience of nature over the authority of tradition, and this perspective opened the way for new scientific investigations of nature.

> *So also this One Thing is an indestructible essence. It is neither hot and dry like Fire, nor cold and moist like Water, nor warm and moist like Air, nor dry and cold like Earth. But it is a skillful perfect equation of all the Elements.*
>
> *- From the book of The Revelation of Hermes as interpreted by Paracelsus*

It is also during this period that alchemists became more sophisticated in their knowledge of chemical processes, and began to introduce ideas and practices that accommodated their discoveries. The four Elements no longer sufficed to explain all material properties, and the three alchemical Essentials of Sulfur, Mercury, and Salt were developed to represent the qualities of combustibility, volatility, and incombustibility, respectively. Although represented by actual physical substances, these Essentials were abstractions of the qualities of matter, just as the four Elements were.

29

As Elemental theory developed and deepened over the centuries, a wealth of correspondences were generated and organized. For example, medieval alchemists believed in Elemental spirits - gnomes (Earth), undines (Water), sylphs (Air), and salamanders (Fire). The four suits of the Tarot deck, whose precise origins are unknown but which has been suggested as an alchemical teaching device, correspond to the Elements, and the shuffling of the deck evocative of the creative process wherein the Elements are brought together (Walker, 1988).

The prominence and centrality of the Elements in Western thought was not challenged until 1661, when Robert Boyle, the founder of modern chemistry, argued that the Elements of the ancient world could not be real chemical elements because they could not be combined to form other substances, nor could they be extracted from other substances. Ironically, both he and Isaac Newton, the founder of modern physics, were known to have been secret alchemists (Non-Fiction, 1995).

### Nature That Framed Us of Four Elements

*Nature that framed us of four elements,*
*Warring within our breast for regiment,*
*Doth teach us all to have aspiring minds:*
*Our souls, whose faculties can comprehend*
*The wondrous architecture of the world,*
*And measure every wandering planet's course,*
*Still climbing after knowledge infinite,*
*And always moving as the restless spheres,*
*Will us to wear ourselves, and never rest,*
*Until we reach the ripest fruit of all,*
*That perfect bliss and sole felicity,*
*The sweet fruition of an earthly crown.*

*- Christopher Marlowe (1564 - 1593)*
*from Tamburlaine the Great, Part I*

# Aboriginal Elements

## The Living Elements.

The Elements as they have evolved in the Western tradition represent a symbol set that is perceived in a way unique to the culture out of which it arose. They are consistently viewed as abstract representations of the qualities of matter, and are generally considered to be of divine origin. Under the influence of many centuries of a rigid hierarchical social order, the relationship between the supernatural Elements and the human beings who worked with them became imbued with the themes of worship, isolation, formal structure, and esoteric knowledge. For example, the medieval European alchemist is often represented as a solitary figure, whose assistant (often female) obeys him explicitly. Alchemical texts often portray the Elements in a context of celestial beings, royal figures, mathematical or geometrical equations, and arcane instructions.

In contrast, Primal cultures tend to experience the Elements in the context of a much different relationship. According to Jamake Highwater (1996), fundamental differences exist between Western and Primal perceptions of reality, and these differing perspectives inform how we encounter the natural world. Because Primal cultures view all things, including human beings, as sacred, the relationship with the Elements is an intimate, familial one. For example, Native American traditions often speak of the wind, trees, and rivers as brothers and sisters, and the earth as Mother. Within this family, humans are not special creatures charged with the task of imposing order on an essentially chaotic natural world, nor the humble custodians of deified forces. Rather, they are children of the land and siblings of all things upon it. From this perspective, the Elements are sacred no more and no less than we are, and a direct undiluted experience of and interaction with them is possible.

In Joseph Campbell's Mythos series (1996), he refers to a letter written by the Native American chief Seattle to the United States government in response to its request to "buy" the land occupied by his tribe. In it, Seattle expresses his consternation that white people consider land as something to be bought and sold, and describes his people's relationship to the Earth as one of children to their mother. He also paints vivid word pictures of the other Elements - Water as the blood of his ancestors, as holding his father's voice, and Air as the wind that gives his people their breath.

Traditional myths of the Navajo and Pueblo tribes depict the human race as arising out of the womb of the Earth, with the other Elements figuring as characters or attributes of characters in many tribal legends. In a classic Navajo sandpainting called *Curtains of the Sky*, the four cardinal directions are correlated with different times of day, seasons, and stages of life (Campbell, 1996). This quadratic depiction of the cosmos with center taken up by a dark abyss echoes the Primal creation myths of civilizations half a world away. Similarly, a Native American song echoes the cyclical nature of Elemental transformation, with the words, "The earth, the water, the fire, the air, Return, return, return, return." (Starhawk, 1989, p.224).

## The Communal Elements.

The Elements are also represented and invoked through other tribal rituals - many agrarian Primal cultures perform rain dances and sun dances, including the Sioux, the South African Angoni, and the Maya. These agricultural dances tend to be abstract in form, in contrast to the mimetic qualities of animal dances. Rain dances usually feature dancing in a circle, greenery, and the pouring of water, while sun dances often took place around a central pole erected to symbolize the Sun as a source of power. In marked contrast to the solitary pursuits of a medieval European alchemist, these Elemental rituals are public events participated in by members of the community at large, and serve a communal as well as an individual function.

A Primal perspective on the natural world also exists in European cultures, although this "old religion" has been almost entirely driven underground by centuries of religious persecution by the Christian church, and by developments in Western philosophy, science, and technology. Remarkably close in spirit to the Native American tradition or the shamanic practices of the

Arctic, this European pagan tradition is based on nature rather than scripture or dogma, and employs communal ritual as a key aspect of its practice (Starhawk, 1989). The four Elements are central to many Wiccan and Druidic rites, and share numerous symbolic connotations with alchemy.

# Distillation and Renewal

The history of symbols as ancient and widespread as the Elements is not easily condensed, but some distillation of critical concepts is essential to understanding the synthesis involved when the alchemical Elements are married to somatic and expressive movement practices. Equally important is translating and updating these ideas if we are to accept alchemical and Elemental concepts as enduringly useful in the creation of our current personal and collective mythologies.

From the Chinese tradition, several significant ideas may be gleaned - the concept of the Elements as related to one another as members of a family, the role of rhythm in the creative process, the cyclic nature of change, and the interaction of polarities as fundamental to differentiation and transformation. The Chinese tradition also offers us the important concept of the human body as a microcosm whose rhythms, cycles, and internal relationship of elements echo the larger universe.

Indian Ayurveda established the Elements as agents of physical healing, and developed a humoral or constitutional framework based upon them. Greek humoral theories echo this concept of the Elements playing a role in bodily functioning and health. The idea that the Elements provide resonant symbolic structures for both physical and psychological phenomena is crucial to the holistic perspective of Elemental Movement .
Primal cultures have also contributed significantly to ways of conceiving of and working with the Elements. In considering all of nature as sacred and alive, this perspective views the Elements as living and our relationship to them as direct and personal (Highwater, 1996). Because primal cultures tend to see the role of

the individual differently than in Western culture, communal ways of working with the Elements are emphasized.

Bringing some of these ideas into the present is easier than one might expect, given their antiquity. Several key concepts are being validated by modern research. For example, the role of rhythm in the process of generating organizational structure is being supported by chaos theory (Bender, 1997). We now recognize that rhythmic vibration underlies all material systems. (The earth's magnetosphere and human brain waves both pulsate at 10 cycles per second. The sun vibrates a dozen octaves below the lowest note on a piano. Human DNA quivers at a billion cycles per second.) We are also beginning to understand how repetitive vibration generates geometric structure - the fractal structures of chaos theory are graphic records of geometries resulting from such a process of repetition and ordered change (Bender, 1997). Clearly, the importance of rhythm in any process of change is becoming acknowledged.

Modern advances in molecular biology have uncovered structural elements of our genetic code that echo the Hippocratic model of the four humors (Marketos, 1997). According to genetic theorists and researchers, the DNA of humans, animals, plants, bacteria, and viruses is based on different combinations of four nucleic bases. Each of these four nucleic bases (adenine, guanine, cytosine, and thymine) is, in turn, created from a mixture of four key elements - carbon, oxygen, hydrogen, and nitrogen. Although obvious differences between these two systems exist, the similar pattern of four basic building blocks raises intriguing questions.

The modern fields of ecopsychology, quantum physics, and holistic medicine also reiterate some of the same ideas shared by early alchemists. Deepak Chopra, trained in both Western and Ayurvedic medicine, asserts that quantum field theorists have reached a conclusion similar to the ancient creation myths - that the raw material of the universe is not solid matter but energy. Behind the "visible garment of the universe" lies a seamless matrix of nothingness - the quintessential and primal Ether (Chopra, 1993, p.26). There is also a growing conviction, shared by many ecopsychologists and expressed by Joseph Campbell (1996), that the Judeo-Christian mythos that has dominated much of Western culture for centuries is dead and needs to be replaced with one that values nature as sacred and our relationship to it as primary and mutual.  Reconnecting with the natural Elements both individually and collectively is one way to renew that relationship.

# Inner Alchemy[4]:

# Elemental Symbols and the Psyche

In order to understand more specifically how the Elements may be employed in a process of personal transformation through movement, two interrelated dimensions of human experience need to be woven into our discussion. The first thread is that of the psyche - those aspects of awareness that relate to human cognition, emotion, and abstraction. The second - the soma - is also concerned with internal experience, but with focus on sensation and kinesthetic awareness. In this section, the alchemical Elements are viewed from a psychological perspective, with an emphasis on their relevance as developmental, relational and symbolic tools. It outlines some of the different ways that symbols generally, and the Elements specifically, may be used as instruments of the psyche in the service of increased awareness. The Elements as instruments of somatic awareness will be discussed in the next chapter.

The word *symbol* comes to us from the Greek, meaning *that which is brought together*. This etymological perspective offers an operational definition, and emphasizes the function of symbols over their form or content. The ability of symbols to act as links - between conscious and unconscious, between self and other, and between different kinds of experience - is one of their most potent characteristics, and the one most utilized by Elemental Movement . A description of the connective capacity of symbols is offered by Johan H. Quanjer (Davis, 1988, p.1):

---

[4] As defined by modern alchemist Adam McLean, Inner Alchemy is alchemy pursued as an interior or soul activity. According to McLean, the main themes explored by Inner Alchemy are the psychological interpretation of alchemy, alchemy as a repository of archetypal images and ideas, working with alchemical imagery as a meditative tool, and the exploration of symbolic material found in alchemy (McLean, 1999).

*A symbol represents an image which links us to the higher levels of subjective intuitive experience as well as to our conscious immediate awareness. It is a midway point between what is 'out there' and what is deeply imbedded within.*

Symbols also possess the ability to link us to each other, and are the most complex of three related components of non-verbal communication processes in humans. These components - signals, signs, and symbols - are found in all known cultures, and are thought to have developed prehistorically, perhaps even predating human attempts at vocal language. Signals are relatively simple devices that serve to attract attention but do not carry any intrinsic meaning. Signs, however, possess inherent specific meaning. For example, a shout is a signal (which may or may not mean "Stop!"), while a red traffic light is a sign (which definitely does mean "Stop!"). The meaning assigned to any given sign depends on the context, and will vary from culture to culture.

The meaning assigned to a symbol, however, may vary from one individual to the next. Rather than eliciting specific meanings, symbols serve to evoke whole patterns of experience, as well as the beliefs, emotions, and values that surround those experiences. As a communication device, symbols depend entirely on the abstractions with which they are imbued by the observer. Despite their potential for ambiguity, symbols are powerful tools of communication, and can actually transform as well as transmit meaning. The philosopher Alfred North Whitehead suggests that symbols are analogs that represent some aspect or quality of experience "...that is enhanced in importance or value by the process of symbolization itself" (Whitehead, 1998). Although individuals respond to symbols in uniquely subjective ways, these metaphors for experience usually reflect a specific cultural logic, and are developed to communicate information between people who have acculturated in common ways. This information may be transmitted through three distinctly recognized types of symbols - the visual symbol, the linguistic symbol, and symbolic action. A group of interactive symbols - such as the Elements - are referred to as an *icon*.

Working with the Elements as symbols is enhanced by a conscious awareness of the capacity of symbols to suggest and evoke very different responses from one individual to the next. For example, Fire might elicit images of raging forest fires in one person and the tranquil flicker of a candle flame in another. Although common threads of meaning will likely emerge, our responses will also be unique to our own personal experience and to our culture. Because symbols are patterns that we create anew each time we experience them, the movements elicited by an Elemental symbol are also unique to that particular moment in time. The group practice of Elemental Movement , therefore, is a here-and-now manifestation of both community and diversity, as the body movements of each member of the group reflect the symbolic responses that are particular to them as well as the responses shared by other members of the group. Extracting meaning from the movements of the group depends on the input of each member, and some consensus on the shared qualities of the action. The importance of this aspect of symbolic improvisation will be discussed further in the section on Processing Movement Experiences.

*As a way to experiment with the differences and similarities evoked by the Elements as symbols, try this exercise with a few other people. Choose an Element, and write down the first ten associations that are evoked for you when you think of this Element. For example, a list of associations for the Element of Water might read, "wet, liquid, cold, thirsty, swim, ocean, salt, fish, waves, boats". Now compare your list with the others. Note common themes, as well as individual ones. Notice your response to finding both commonality and diversity of meanings. If you repeated this experiment in three months time, you can probably imagine that the data you collect would be slightly different, even though the experiment and the subjects remain the same. Working with symbols is always a process of creating meaning, rather than simply accessing or recalling meaning.*

# Elemental Building Blocks

Cognitively, symbols form part of a set of structures involved in the acquisition, processing, organization, and use of information, and are dependent upon the mental ability to create and recognize arbitrary abstract representations of an experience. As a cognitive structure, symbols are used to create *concepts*, a particular type of symbol that represents a set of attributes common to a group of symbols, and that is used to sort specific experiences into categories of experience.

The stages of cognitive development first postulated by Swiss psychologist Jean Piaget are based on the individual's progressive ability to use symbols and concepts in their interactions with the environment. According to Piaget, the ability to manipulate the environment through symbolic thought and action does not usually begin to occur until the age of two, followed several years later by the development of logic and the ability to reason (Bee, 1985). However, these developmental theories reflect a presupposed division between cognition and emotion that some later theorists dispute. Stanley Greenspan (1997), accentuating the role of affect and interaction in child development, suggests that the effective use of symbols becomes possible only when emotional/sensory integration, intimacy, and intentionality are first established. Greenspan notes that it is at this same stage of development that inner representations of the self are created, allowing for the eventual construction of a cohesive and functioning internal world. By extension, the intentional and systematic use of the Elements as symbols may serve to foster the development of more complex and fully-articulated internal representations of the self. The theories of play articulated in the following section offer some additional thoughts as to how this process of personal development might take place.

# Elemental Child's Play

Symbols are more than just tools of self-organization and communication - they are also tools of relationship. Object relations theory suggests that a crucial stage in child development occurs when the child is able to form a relationship with a transitional object (Winnicott, 1971). This transitional object (such as a favorite toy or blanket) is employed by the child as a means of gradually detaching from the primary object (usually the parent or primary caregiver) en route to the developmental goal of independence. As the child matures, the transitional object is relinquished.

In contrast to the linear developmental progression from dependence to autonomy described by traditional object relations theorists, D.W. Winnicott (1971) suggests that the transitional stage between attachment and independence, symbolized by the transitional object, is actually a fertile playground for personal exploration, and need not be relinquished utterly in pursuit of maturity. He argues that this stage of child's play may be expanded to include many forms of creative and artistic expression, and that it is through the playful imaginations of the transitional space that the fundamental psychological paradoxes of subject/object, me/not me, and real/not real may be experienced and understood. The transitional space of play, therefore, is neither inside or outside the self. It takes up space and time in the objective external world, yet it is still partly under the magical control of the individual's own imagination.

Because it is within this transitional, or play, space that much of the psychological exploration of Elemental Movement takes place, a fuller description of the significant factors of play is in order. First, the play state involves a high degree of focus and absorption. True play is not easily abandoned, nor outside stimuli easily admitted. (Neitzsche suggests that adults reach maturity when they are able to recapture the seriousness of a child at play [Powers, 1998]). Second, the play space is the location where objects and phenomena from external reality are employed in the service of some fragment of inner subjective reality. In play, this piece of personal reality is lived with, experienced in a setting created out of chosen aspects of the outside world. The freedom of choice inherent in the structure of play allows changes to be made to inner material by manipulating it externally. Third, the unseen dimensions of the psyche are made more visible through the interplay of subjective and objective phenomena. This external visibility creates the possibility of analysis and reflection both by the individual or by an observing therapist. However, Winnicott emphasizes the importance of not offering interpretations "outside the ripeness of the material" (Winnicott, 1971, p.51), or if the individual has no desire or capacity to play. Lastly, play takes on a therapeutic dimension only when it is entered into spontaneously, and not out of a wish to comply with the expectations of another.

The same factors at work in the play experience can also be said to operate in cultural or artistic experience (Winnicott, 1971). By playing with objective reality and coloring it with the creativity of our own imaginations, we suffuse it with poetry. Provided we do not insist on the objectivity of our subjective phenomena, we can enjoy its richness, and even find pleasure in discovering places where our transitional spaces meet with the transitional spaces of others. This sense of shared imagination is the bond felt by playmates immersed in the same game of make-believe as well as the connection felt by members of a group in art, religion, or philosophy (Winnicott, 1971).

According to Mihaly Csiksentmihalyi (1975), play also possesses intrinsic rewards beyond its capacity to offer a medium for self-exploration, most significantly a pleasurable state common to many play activities which he calls *flow*. Although any activity may produce flow experiences, some activities - such as the play intrinsic to the transitional stage - offer better opportunities for generating flow than others. A limited field of stimuli, clear structure, and the opportunity to challenge oneself are key factors. Described as a whole-body sensation experienced when acting with total involvement, the flow experience tends to merge action and awareness, stimulus and response, and self and environment into a unified, connected event.

Playing with the Elements - through spontaneous movement improvisation and through structured symbolic activity - facilitates the discriminating boundary explorations of the transitional stage as well as the integrating potential of the flow experience. Although not likely to be chosen by a child as an original transitional object, the Elements offer a wide range of qualities with which to compare and contrast a developing sense of unique personal identity. In choosing an Element as the fragment of objective reality in which our creative play is set, we can use it to embody and transform aspects of our inner subjective reality.

As a process, Elemental Movement also provides an opportunity to enhance feelings of connection and relationship through shared experiences in the transitional space, and through the generation of flow. Using the Elements as a basis for creating flow experiences will be articulated in more detail in the description of contemplative movement in the section dealing with the Element of Ether. In particular, group unison movement structures often provide the clear structure and limited field of stimulus so key to the experience of flow.

*Here are some ideas for simple Elemental games to play with a partner as a way to explore how the Elements can be used as transitional objects: 1) Create an earth sculpture with a partner. Without words, mold and shape a single lump of clay together. 2) Using a glass of water (for you) and an empty glass (for your partner), pour the water back and forth between the two of you. Play with speed and distance. 3) Using just your breath, keep a small fluffy feather aloft in the air between you and your partner. Or use your hands to keep a balloon in the air. 4) In a darkened room, create a firelight pas de deux with two flashlight (or laser pointer) beams on the walls and ceiling.*

# Elemental Screens

The psychological mechanism of *projection* is also active in the process of working with the Elements as symbols. Defined as "a trait, attitude, feeling, or bit of behavior which actually belongs to your own personality but is not experienced as such" (Perls et al, 1980), a projection allows us to disown aspects of ourselves we are unable or unwilling to acknowledge as ours. Usually, the tendency to project certain aspects of experience or behavior develops in response to cultural norms or parental restrictions. In an effort to conform to the expectations of the environment, we unconsciously reject aspects of our selves that we imagine others would also reject were we to reveal them. Of course, it is not actually possible to eradicate personal traits simply by wishing them away, and the feelings generated by these unwanted aspects of self continue to haunt us. Unwilling to locate the source of these feelings inside ourselves, we externalize the source of our feelings by projecting them onto an appropriate object in the environment.

Projection offers a temporary distance from disowned aspects of self, but only reowning and integrating the disowned material allows the individual to responsibly and fully experience themselves as they are. By acknowledging traits that we imagine others will censure, we reopen the option of choosing for ourselves how to be, and allow ourselves an expanded repertoire of awareness and experience. Conscious, deliberate projection may be employed therapeutically in an effort to illuminate unconscious projection, and is basic to many creative and expressive arts approaches to therapy.

Because of their kaleidoscopic and relatively transparent nature, the Elements serve as useful screens for conscious projective work. The following exercise illustrates how they may be used to explore aspects of the self through the process of projection:

Choose one of the five Elements - Earth, Water, Air, Fire, or Ether - and imagine a small area directly in front of you is filled with that Element. Picture the Element in your mind's eye as clearly as you can, and begin to describe it aloud as if it were alive. For example, "Earth, you are heavy. You are dense and solid. You are serious and stubborn." (Notice the personification in the last statement - this tendency to anthropomorphize is natural, and is part of what makes this exercise effective.) Do not strain to interpret your description, or to impose meaningful connections. Simply notice what you imagine the significant qualities of that Element to be, and remain aware of your emotional responses as you speak. After you have finished describing the Element, move into the space where you imagined the Element to be, and take on the role of the Element. Describe yourself as that Element, as if

43

*you now possessed the same significant qualities you previously noted in the Element. When you have finished, notice your response to the exercise.*

# Elemental Archetypes

Of all the ways in which the alchemical Elements serve as psychological symbols, perhaps none is more complex and fully articulated than the *archetype*, a particular kind of symbol developed by the Swiss psychoanalyst Carl Jung. Jung has been pivotal in making connections between alchemy and psychology in this century, and in reviving public and professional interest in the field. His fascination with the subject area arose through the discovery that his analysands were producing symbols in their dreams and artwork similar to those found in ancient alchemical texts, and eventually led to his elaboration of the concept of a *collective unconscious* as the means whereby these symbolic images were shared across both culture and time.

Jung postulates the existence of a common genetic stock rooted in the distant past from which all lines of psychological development branch. Just as all homo sapiens share similar anatomical features irrespective of race or culture, so does the human psyche possess a common substratum of instincts, unconscious tendencies and latent predispositions (Jung, 1967). Distinct from the *personal unconscious* (that part of the unaware mind containing impulses and memories originating in individual experience), the collective unconscious is common to all humankind, and is based on the genetically-inherited structure of the brain. According to Jung, it is the existence of this common psychic structure that explains the similarity in myth motifs across cultures.

Central to the anatomy of the collective unconscious is the archetype - a primal pattern that allows the individual to organize perception and experience and respond to it in a meaningful way. According to Jung, archetypes form a symbolic network which the mind projects onto experience to introduce order to it. In much the same way as the ancient alchemists perceived of the Elements, archetypes are more pattern than product, more property than object. They are abstractions, used much the same way that modern physicists use the concepts of energy, particle, or time-space continuum in order to understand the intangible world of subatomic behavior.

In addition to their role in conceptualizing experience, archetypes are also involved in a process of psychological transformation and integration, called *individuation,* that actually changes the nature of individual awareness. In *Alchemical Studies* (1967), Jung asserts that by consciously realizing the polarities hidden in the unconscious a new level of consciousness, or individuation, is attained. This union of opposites is a process of personality development that is expressed through archetypal symbols.

Individuation is not simply a matter of manipulating archetypes, however. Jung (1967) discusses the attitude of the practitioner as critical to the process of inner alchemy, and suggests that most people do not understand the art of allowing psychic processes to develop naturally, but rather insist on helping, correcting, and generally interfering with them. Rather, individuals should learn how to simply observe how a fragment of spontaneous imagination develops. This process of engaged but nondirective psychological exploration Jung called *active imagination,* and it forms the basis of Jungian expressive arts therapy theory and practice (Storr, 1983).

According to Jung, objective self-reflection is also critical to the integration of unconscious material, and he considers it an important therapeutic goal (Jung, 1967). He characterizes this perspective as a degree of conscious detachment from the world to the point where consciousness is no longer preoccupied with or dominated by it. In contrast, significant non-differentiation between subject and object results in a sort of *participation mystique* with the environment, in which the unconscious is projected onto the object, and the object subsequently introjected into the subject. In early primal cultures, women and men so identified themselves with nature that they could not be said to exist as self-conceived individuals in the same way that we do today (Winnicott, 1971). This enmeshment with the object is reflected in plants and animals being unconsciously assigned human attributes (and vice versa).

In contrast, individuation is the conscious process of identifying and integrating archetypal material as it reveals itself.

Archetypes manifest differently depending upon the individual and upon their degree of integration into consciousness. When archetypes are experienced as thoughts, they often take the form of intuitively perceived laws or principles, and are initially personified. As Jung describes it, the process of integrating unconscious elements of the personality parallels that encountered in religious phenomenology (1976). Activated unconscious contents appear first as personified projections, and are then gradually assimilated into consciousness as personified ideas, and then as abstract ones. As archetypes, the Elements have undergone a similar evolution through history, moving from "god-like" anthropomorphisms to descriptive attributes.

When archetypes are expressed graphically, they tend to appear as *mandalas*, or magic circles. Mandalas, such as the Navajo sandpainting described in the section on Ancient Alchemy, are often composed of four sections that surround a central core, and may take the form of a flower, a cross, or a wheel. Jung notes that these mandalas may be danced rather than drawn, and that a mandala dance, or *mandala nrithya*, is found in East Indian folk tradition. The effect of the production of such symbolic devices is twofold - not only is the mandala a means of expression, but it also makes an impression upon its creator. Thus, the projection of psychic events exerts a counter-effect that directs attention back toward inner experience. The circular form of the mandala is a significant expression of the psychic and alchemical process of *circumambulatio*. This circulation is more than movement in a circle - it marks off and encloses psychic territory, directs focus, and facilitates the process of incorporating and integrating diverse or polarized elements of the personality (Jung, 1967).

# An Elemental Mandala

*Figure 1*

*The traditional Celtic motif in the figure at left represents the four Elements of which all life consists.  The design is partitioned into quadrants that denote each Element, while the knot itself symbolizes Ether or spirit - that which unites the Elements into a balanced whole.  Similar mandalas have been found on stone carvings in Perthshire, Scotland, and at other ancient Celtic sites.  The pagan religion of the Celts, Druidism, employs the same Elements as Wicca and other primal forms of spiritual practice (see Aboriginal Elements).*

According to Jung, inner alchemists considered the four Elements as the basic constituents of the ultimate alchemical symbol, the *philosopher's stone*.  He suggests that the unified Elements represented the attainment of a balanced, integrated, and refined psychological state, and equates the alchemical quaternary and its reduction to unity with the process of individuation (Jung, 1967).  In a more detailed description, Von Franz (1992) likens individuation to the alchemical process of transforming Earth to Water, Water to Air, Air to Fire, and Fire back to Earth.  On an inner level, this circular process is experienced as the body (Earth) being moved by feeling (Water), feeling supporting thinking (Air), thinking stirring the spirit (Fire), and the spirit being embodied (back to Earth).  The structure of Elemental Movement  echoes this process, using active imagination and the Elemental archetypes as instruments of psychological exploration and integration.

# Patterns and Links

The recurring themes of Inner Alchemy are centered on the idea of the Elements as psychological patterns, and on their ability to make connections.  As a communication device, the Elements evoke patterns of common experience that create links between members of the human community.  As a developmental tool, they can be used to "play" with notions of self and other, and to articulate relationships.  And as archetypes, the Elements are collectively-held motifs that embody the essential qualities of self, and, when integrated, represent a balanced diversity of conscious psychological attributes.

Elemental Movement  draws upon the power of the Elements as symbols of the psyche, and the structure and processing of movement experiences includes the awareness of the psychological dimension at work in movement.  Movement also accesses another important facet of human experience - the somatic dimension - and the next section will offer an overview of the theory of Somatic Alchemy  as it applies to the development of Elemental Movement  .

# Somatic Alchemy

As stated in the Introduction, Somatic Alchemy  is the theoretical and methodological framework in which the practice of Elemental Movement  is grounded.  It is the set of ideas that informs the set of movement structures used in Elemental Movement  . As a conceptual model, it draws upon some of the basic assumptions of both somatics and alchemy, and offers one account of how movement acts as a catalyst for change.  This chapter will describe some of the fundamental tenets of Somatic Alchemy  and outline the meta-process of the transformation it is intended to evoke.

In accordance with the objectives of both art and science, Somatic Alchemy  strives to understand lived human experience. While this experience remains an intangible mystery on many levels, it is important to keep in mind that the whole idea of "experience" is also a human construct.  In deciding what constitutes experience, we bring our own set of biases to bear on what information gets included and emphasized.  For example, women's experience has traditionally been excluded from the larger arena of recognized human experience (Johnson and Ferguson, 1990).  One of the tasks of feminism has been to include the female dimension into social consciousness as well as into the fields of history, psychology, medicine, etc.  Similarly, a somatic perspective understands that the construction of lived bodily experience has been culturally and historically inadequate (Johnson, 1995).  Whether that experience was demonized, sexualized, or trivialized, it has remained peripheral.  Because the experience of the living body has so rarely been a direct focus of theoretical attention, a whole spectrum of human life remains to be discovered.

It is this active process of discovery in which Somatic Alchemy  is engaged, and, as a theory, it is fundamentally experiential.  It is designed to bring into awareness facets of our experience previously unacknowledged or unknown.  In much the same way that the narratives of women's lives serve to inform feminist theory, unearthing the stories of the lived experience of the body acts as a form of consciousness raising that is essential to the theory building of Somatic Alchemy . In a departure from a conventional scientific procedure in which practice proceeds out of theory, the theory of Somatic Alchemy also develops out of practice. Although Elemental Movement was developed specifically to embody the guiding principles of change described in Somatic Alchemy , it also provides a set of movement structures that elicit experiences which reciprocally inform the theory base of Somatic Alchemy .

Other movement and body-centered approaches also contribute to its theoretical framework, and could rightly be considered forms of Somatic Alchemy . Essentially, any model that uses the subjective awareness of the living body as the basis for a process of change in which the differentiated elements of that awareness are integrated, balanced, and transformed is a form of Somatic Alchemy . For example, the internally-focused *neidan* schools of Chinese Alchemy use their perception of the ebb and flow of *yin* and *yang* in the body to realize the nature of the universe and the omnipresent cosmic pattern called the Tao (Pregadio, 1996) . The *movement-in-depth* work developed by American dance therapist and Jungian analyst Mary Whitehouse uses movement as a way to allow undifferentiated and unconscious archetypal material to emerge and become integrated into conscious awareness (Whitehouse, 1963).

However, for these or other approaches to be considered forms of Somatic Alchemy using our definition, two essential criteria must be met. First, the approach must be somatic - that is, it must rely on the internal felt sense of the body as the basis for working with and understanding lived human experience. Among other things, this means that the domain undergoing a process of transformation is what and how we feel inside our own bodies, not how our bodies look or perform from an objective standpoint. Second, the process or tools of change must be alchemical in nature. That is, the transformation of somatic experience must be based on a process that employs the same universal principles of change sought by alchemists across cultures and throughout the ages. These ideas - differentiation, interaction, integration, and contextualization - have been touched upon in previous sections, and underlie an alchemical basis for understanding the nature of change.

50

Described below are six assumptions that form the beginning of a theoretical and methodological framework of Somatic Alchemy . Together, they form a constellation of ideas about the body/mind and change that integrates two unique but overlapping perspectives - the somatic paradigm and the alchemical paradigm. Although there exists no single source for delineating and classifying the beliefs, values, and attitudes of either somatics or alchemy, the principles below represent an adaptation and synthesis of some of the assumptions I have found to be generally shared within these communities. These concepts are also reflective of my own clinical and philosophical orientation, and reveal a wide but often overlapping range of influences - existentialism, phenomenology, gestalt psychology, and feminism.

# Basic Theoretical Concepts of Somatic Alchemy

> *The mind/body issue is not simply a theoretical speculation, but is originally a practical, lived experience...The theoretical is only a reflection on the lived experience.*
>
> *Yuasa Yasuo, in Johnson, 1999, p.1*

1. The *soma* is a living laboratory/workshop for ongoing research into the nature of reality.
2. Movement is the principal experimental method of that research.
3. The primary research data originates out of somatic experience.
4. Experiments are based on alchemical principles and processes of change.
5. The results of this research, and their interpretation, are unique to each soma.
6. All somas are interconnected.

# 1.  The soma is a living laboratory/workshop for ongoing research into the nature of reality.

## What is the Soma?

Thomas Hanna, founder of the field of somatics in the United States, defines the *soma* - after the Greek word meaning living body - as the body as experienced from within (1988). The definition draws its inspiration from Husserl's "somatology", a study of the relationships between direct bodily knowing and scientific knowledge about the body (Johnson, 1999).  An expanded definition of *soma* might be the **body/mind as experienced from within**, as a somatic paradigm is essentially holistic (Greene, 1997).  It understands awareness, biological function, and environment as indivisible aspects of a synergistic whole, and emphasizes the unity of body and mind.  From a somatic perspective, phenomena traditionally regarded as being primarily either physical or psychological are seen as functionally identical (Kepner, 1987).

In contrast, the dualistic model of nineteenth-century Western intellectual tradition separated body and mind, and devalued the body and its perceptions as unreliable and illusory (Murphy, 1969).  In a philosophical legacy extending from Plato and Socrates through to Descartes, the physical senses were regarded as imperfect instruments in perceiving the objective truth of external reality.  Only the mind was considered capable of accurately discerning and understanding the true essence of existence.  Bodily experience was actually thought to inhibit and impair our attempts to understand the nature of reality.

## The Somatic Nature of Reality

Somatics, then, represents a significant departure from conventional ways of thinking about the body and reality.  It draws upon existential, evolutionary, and phenomenological perspectives to suggest that we do more than simply perceive reality through our bodily senses; reality is constructed by the way in which we perceive it (Greene, 1997). This reality construct requires both sensory and cognitive perception. Body and mind are not separately functioning entities, but are connected through the integrative function of perception that relates us to our environment. Therefore, what we experience as reality depends on the quality of somatic perception we bring to our engagement with the world. Because perception determines reality, reality changes as the soma changes. Rather than detracting from the authenticity of our data, the sensory perceptions of our bodily experience are essential to any inquiry into the nature of reality.

In the same way that our sensory and cognitive perceptions create an integrated somatic experience of our external environment, "body" and "mind" also work together to help weave the perceptual fabric of our internal environment. This inner world includes awareness of our internal biological functioning as well as our psychological reality - ideas, emotions, imagination, and beliefs. The psyche is not seen as a separate system with distinct components and self-contained dynamics. Rather, it is one of many facets of somatic experience, and its nature changes with the soma. This idea is important to our understanding of Somatic Alchemy . As a culture, we are not accustomed to expecting changes in our psychological environment as a result of making changes in the bodily one - especially when that change many only consist of a shift in awareness, rather than overt behavior.

Although the process of Somatic Alchemy works largely through the body, the area of investigation is much broader than the dimension we usually think of as physical. In a guest editorial for the Winter 1999 issue of The Somatics Society newsletter, Judyth Weaver describes a somatic approach as emphasizing not the body, but the balance and integration of body and mind. Further, in working with the body, "we address not only the mechanical, physical body, but the engaged body, the one that feels and connects us with our emotions, memories, our whole selves" (p.1). Thus, when we speak of Somatic Alchemy working with the soma as a laboratory, the research being conducted involves explorations and transformations in the nature of our whole human experience. A change in one aspect of our experience affects all the others. Our perceptions of the external environment affect our perceptions of the inner one. Shifts in physical musculature create adjustments in our emotional state. Changes in sensory phenomena inform changes in cognitive perceptions which, in turn, affect our relationship to the environment. And, ultimately, our engagement with the environment both forms and informs reality.

## What is "Somatic" Research?

The process of Somatic Alchemy is inherently experimental, and this exploratory approach is key to understanding the nature of the process and the changes it evokes. Despite general acceptance of modern scientific notions of experimentation in Western culture, a truly experimental attitude toward personal development and well-being is uncommon. In my experience, we are more accustomed to our role as consumers of the results of scientific experimentation, rather than as active investigators. Even the designated agents of personal change - the educators, therapists, and practitioners - often see themselves primarily not as researchers, but as service providers.

For example, many established therapeutic or educational processes rely upon objective assessment or diagnosis as the basis upon which a treatment plan or curriculum is developed. Based on the results of these tests, it is determined whether you are missing components essential to your optimum functioning, and which of them you lack. A plan is then prepared to allow you to acquire these components, whether it is a training regimen, a series of lessons, or a course of therapy. If the diagnosis is correct, following the treatment plan should result in improved functioning. As a model of change, these kinds of prescriptive processes tend to treat the soma objectively and mechanistically. A trained observer will determine what you need, and if you are compliant with treatment, your soma will respond in the manner predicted, following the laws of cause and effect. Although such prescriptive processes for change are often based on prior research, they are not themselves experimental in nature.

In contrast, Somatic Alchemy encourages a different approach to personal development - one that values the active questioning stance of the scientist, combined with the unique values and perspectives of a somatic paradigm. This approach encourages us to develop our own lines of somatic inquiry based on subjective assessment and individually determined goals. We decide for ourselves what and how we want to learn and change, and we understand that awareness itself is a form of change. Like any field of study, Somatic Alchemy draws upon the findings of previous research, but it emphasizes the subjective nature of somatic data, and less reliance on established norms of human behavior. It recognizes that the soma is a complex and largely uncharted territory, and that an exploratory research strategy may yield more fruitful results than one that requires the formulation of too-specific goals, methods, or indicators of success. Without completely reinventing the wheel in terms of accessing and utilizing our common body of knowledge, it nonetheless allows individuals to take greater responsibility for our own experience of change. Instead of passively submitting to a prescribed course of action, we become the creators of our own process of somatic self-discovery. Given the Western cultural emphasis on objective achievement and adherence to norms, an experimental attitude with regard to somatic development offers a unique, and potentially radical, opportunity for empowerment.

## 2. Movement is the primary instrument and medium of that research.

The open-ended research strategy of Somatic Alchemy allows it to incorporate a range of research designs and methodologies. We can explore the soma through survey, mapping the territory by charting all the answers our body tells us in response to the questions we ask. We can walk ourselves through our own case histories, remembering how it felt to be stung by a bee, or swim in the ocean, or take a nap in the sun. We can also explore the soma by moving in the moment, using our ability to move as the key to an experiment. For example, a very simple somatic experiment might begin with the felt awareness of tension and fatigue. If the movement of yawning and stretching was applied, most of us would likely experience a perceptible shift in our somatic experience in response. Although the soma is affected on many levels by any number of factors - environmental conditions, biochemical changes - voluntary body movement is one factor over which we usually have a degree of control. Because we can direct it, movement is a useful independent variable in conducting somatic experiments. It also makes an effective survey question - *How do I feel when I move like this?* - and a flexible instrument for heuristic inquiry.

Another reason for using movement as the research medium in Somatic Alchemy is because of its power to reveal and affect us on many dimensions of experience. Movement is both functional (we use it to get what we need) and expressive (we use it to show how we feel). It is both voluntary and involuntary, and occurs on conscious and unconscious levels. Because it crosses over many of these boundaries, movement is ideally suited to the task of exploring the soma - the intersecting physical, psychological, and interpersonal aspects of experience - and fostering the holistic integration of the individual (Lewis, 1987).

Mary Whitehouse, a pioneer in the field of dance/movement therapy, asserts that, for most people, physical movement is automatic, unconscious, and organized toward an objective goal (Whitehouse, 1963). We need to speak to a friend, so we reach for the phone. We need a book, so we walk over to get it. We need a quart of milk and to get in shape, so we jog to the store. In a culture that stresses goal-orientation, it follows that movement is often regarded as a means to an end. Consequently, how we move, and what we reveal about ourselves in the quality of those movements is not usually part of our awareness. We rarely consider movement as a process, or consider the possibility of using the awareness of movement to facilitate changes not only in our movement behavior, but in other areas of our experience as well. By attending to movement as a process, Somatic Alchemy seeks to evoke changes in both the functional and expressive dimensions of movement. Movement's ability to reveal these dual aspects of somatic experience is perhaps its most powerful attribute as an instrument of somatic inquiry. The awakening awareness of how one moves leads gradually to a recognition of how our movement is a reflection of the soma as a whole.

On a functional level, this awareness allows us to enhance the ease and effectiveness of our movements by making changes at the source. Take the bodily motion of reaching as an example. Ordinarily, the object of our reaching is the sole focus of our attention. Attending to the act of reaching itself encourages us to notice whether we experience the movement as comfortable and efficient, and to develop strategies for improving it if needed. For example, tension and restriction in reaching with the arms may relate to an unconscious omission in anchoring the movement with the lower body (Woodruff, 1991). Bringing awareness to the whole soma while reaching allows this information to be uncovered and addressed.

On an expressive level, conscious attention to movement allows us to begin to ask questions about what that movement reveals about us as personalities (Whitehouse, 1963). Regardless of its functionality, the motion of reaching is also emotive. Through a simple extension of the arm, we can convey longing, triumph, panic, or despair. Although we rarely attend consciously to its expressive dimension, individually and collectively, movement is our most primal form of communication (Whitehouse, 1963). Before we formed words to convey our experience, we uttered it with our bodies - movement speaks to us clearly in the insistent probing of a hungry infant, or the frenzied stamping of a tribal war dance. Movement is our mother tongue - although personal, cultural and historical dialects exist, we all possess the same basic ability to speak and understand the language of movement. Even after the development of sophisticated verbal language skills, movement remains our clearest and most reliable line of communication. Research indicates that up to 70 percent of daily interpersonal communication takes place non-verbally, and that when a verbal statement is contradicted by an underlying non-verbal message, it is the non-verbal message we trust (Blom and Chaplin, 1988).

Despite its primacy and universality, human movement is also highly individual and complex. Some of our movement skills are based on innate developmental patterns; others reflect motor responses to learning experiences throughout our lives (Cohen, 1993). The way we move is as unique to us as our fingerprint, and our movement patterns offer a singular reflection of our personal and genetic history. Each of us moves from our own anatomical, physiological, and psychological framework, and our movements reveal a unique use of space, effort, intention, shaping, and pattern. Professionals engaged in the work of analyzing and recording movement require elaborate systems of notation to capture even the most basic elements of a gesture, gait, or action (Bartenieff, 1988). Movement's complexity offers us a rich source of information about our somatic reality.

The richness of movement as a medium of expression and exploration has made it an important tool for many who study the inner dimensions of human experience. Both internal alchemists and somaticists often use some form of movement as the means whereby personal experimentation is carried out. The graceful flow of Taoist T'ai Chi[5] and the watery undulations of Emilie Conrad Da'oud's Continuum[6] work each explore different facets of somatic experience through movement. Although one is an ancient form of inner alchemy and the other a modern somatic practice, both understand movement as a medium for the expression of universal principles.

## 3. The primary research data originates out of somatic experience.

*Our cells have intelligence. If we take the time to listen, they can be trusted to respond.*

*- Frances Becker (1993, p.54)*

---

[5] T'ai Chi, also known as T'ai Chi Chuan, is a Taoist movement practice based on the principle of balance between the polarized forces of yin and yang. It is designed to stimulate and echo the flow of chi, or life energy, in the body (Kastner, 1996).

[6] A fundamental premise of Continuum is that we carry the movement of water in every cell of our body, and the wave motion is basic to all living creatures. (Kastner, 1996).

As a somatic approach, Somatic Alchemy privileges the first-person experience of the body. It emphasizes not how a particular movement experiment affects the way the soma looks or behaves, but how it affects the way the soma feels. Although the process of Somatic Alchemy may also effect changes in the externally observable body, these changes are secondary to the primary changes occurring on the level of internal awareness. This does not mean that cognitive analysis or outwardly perceived behavior has no place in the research process, it simply means that subjective somatic experience is considered foremost. Any conclusions arising from the research must include, and not significantly contradict, that data. From a research standpoint, somatic experience is the main dependent variable in a movement experiment. Although other dependent variables - emotions, images, behavior, ideas, other sensory impressions - are included in the raw data, they are considered in light of their relationship to somatic experience. When they are congruent with it, they support the conclusions drawn in assessing the effect of the experiment on somatic experience. When they contradict somatic experience, further investigation is called for.

Because the soma is an integrative and interactive process of the body/mind in relation to the environment, the full gamut of somatic experience occurs on many levels. Somatic experience is one dimension of that larger awareness, and usually refers to the mainly kinesthetic and proprioceptive data created by the nervous system (Kastner, 1996). This information is moderated by the sensory/motor cortex and includes sensations such as tightness, heaviness, warmth, pleasure, pain, numbness, lightness, expansion, etc.

We may also experience body-centered emotional reactions (fury, elation, anxiety) and feeling-state interpretations (invaded, safe, abandoned) in connection with our somatic experience. Because our central nervous system co-ordinates sensory information from other systems, other senses often contribute data - we can hear as well as feel our breath, smell as well as feel our skin, taste as well as feel our saliva, and see as well as feel our movements. Although these sensations and feelings are essential dimensions of our overall experience, they should not be mistaken or substituted for somatic experience.

The specific emphasis on somatic experience as the primary data of our research can present a challenge for the researcher/participant. Many of us have not developed our kinesthetic and proprioceptive senses beyond basic requirements for successful locomotion and manipulation. The felt dimension of our own body stories is largely unspoken, and the specialized tools for elaborating these narratives are not cultivated. Without these fundamental facilities, the self-discovery of our own bodies is hampered. Not only is somatic experience the primary source of research data in our living experiment, it is also the most important method of observation. Only by directing our awareness to our somatic experience (kinesthetically "observing" our dependent variable) can we discern changes in that experience.

Somatic approaches offer different ways of discovering the body and developing the tools of somatic experience. The Sensory Awareness work of Charlotte Selver works to illuminate and clarify faint impressions from within the soma through simple inquiry and quiet inner attentiveness (Johnson, 1993). Some Eastern meditation practices attend to the breath as a way to enhance awareness of the bodily sensations that arise with the movement of breathing (Knaster, 1996). Peter Levine's *Somatic Experiencing* uses directed touch, imagery, and movement patterns to facilitate what he calls the felt sense (Levine, 1997). Elemental Movement is also designed to cultivate the instruments of our somatic experience, using imagery, inquiry, and movement in combination with the Elements to explore the less familiar dimension of somatic awareness.

### An Experiment in Somatic Experience
(from *Waking the Tiger* by Peter Levine, 1997)

- Feel the way your body makes contact with the surface that is supporting you.
- Sense into your skin and notice the way your clothes feel.
- Sense underneath your skin - what sensations are there?

- Now, gently remembering these sensations, how do you know that you feel comfortable? What physical sensations contribute to the overall feeling of comfort?
- Does becoming more aware of these sensations make you feel more or less comfortable? Does this change over time?

Somatic experience is critical to the research in which Somatic Alchemy is engaged because of its relationship to the soma's ability to change. Deane Juhan, a somatic practitioner and author of *Job's Body*, explains that until we have direct and concrete knowledge about our soma's condition and situation, we are in no position to make meaningful, comprehensive, and effective changes within it. He asserts that we literally feel our way through the process of change, and that new sensory information is necessary in order to create new ways of being (Juhan, 1987). This process can be compared to the sensory feedback loops the central nervous system relies upon to make functional changes in the somatic environment. Input travels as electrochemical impulses from the nerve endings to the brain, which in turn sends out impulses that effect change, which is picked up by the nerve endings, which sends this new information to the brain, which makes adjustments based on the updated information, and sends out new directives. It is evident that without input, this feedback loop is disabled, and change is impossible. With distorted or incomplete input, attempts to make satisfying changes are unsuccessful. In Somatic Alchemy , somatic experience is the input necessary to initiate the feedback loop that creates changes in the somatic environment.

Not only is somatic feedback necessary to somatic change, it is also a vital source of information about the general functioning of our larger field of consciousness. As Juhan (1999) explains, the healthily functioning organism is often paradoxically unaware of the underlying biological operations that create and support consciousness. When the soma is operating smoothly to produce a clear field of consciousness, we are usually aware only of the field, not the elements that produce it. This tendency of the soma to "disappear" from awareness raises the risk of becoming identified with and lost in the virtual reality of disembodied consciousness, and to experience consciousness as having little to do with the organism that is producing it. This somatic dissociation can lead to distortions of consciousness unless we are in possession of the tools of awareness that can warn us when something in the organism that is producing consciousness is amiss. Somatic awareness allows us to calibrate our instruments of consciousness. By cross-checking our thoughts, impulses, and beliefs with the somatic feedback that tells us how we *feel* when we are experiencing those dimensions of consciousness, we anchor them.

## 4. Experiments are based on somatic and alchemical principles of change.

The alchemical and somatic processes of change described here represent only a fraction of the hundreds of concepts and methods these multiform fields of practice employ. Despite the uniqueness that clearly distinguishes the work of an Ayurvedic doctor from that of a medieval European alchemist or a modern practitioner of Body-Mind Centering, common threads run through many of these disciplines. It is these common threads I have tried to gather and weave together in describing the overall process of Somatic Alchemy . Each of these threads describe both a concept and a process, and work together to form the meta-process of change. These threads - differentiation, interaction, integration, and contextualization are presented here in sequence, although they often overlap in an interwoven progression.

Key to understanding the choice and ordering of these particular threads is the fact that, as a somatic approach, Somatic Alchemy views the individual holistically - as a whole greater than the sum of its inter-related parts (Greene, 1997). However they are defined - as body, mind, and spirit, or thoughts and feelings, or different aspects of self - these parts are seen in a context in which each of these dimensions is valued for its contribution to the whole individual. As a holistic model, it also recognizes that the individual s integrity, ability, and capacity for growth is enhanced by the awareness and functional integration of all aspects of the self (Rosner, 1987). Differentiation, interaction, integration, and contextualization are steps to that holistic goal.

## Differentiation

Differentiation refers to the process of distinguishing the unique elements within a larger unified whole. Although the whole is recognized as larger than the sum of its parts, understanding the individual parts contributes to the understanding of the whole. The act of discerning one element from another requires us to explore its unique qualities, and teaches us about its particular properties and functions. Differentiation is an organic part of the learning process in humans, and examples of it abound in our daily experience. Children naturally attempt differentiation before integration - they will learn to take a puzzle apart long before they learn how to put it back together (Stokes, 1998).

On a body level, the Fundamentals® work of Irmgard Bartenieff recognizes the importance of differentiation as a precursor to functional integration (Bartenieff, 1980). One exercise requires movement that differentiates clearly between two halves of the body - left and right sides - and can be remarkably challenging to execute. The Five-Rhythms work of Gabrielle Roth also exemplifies the process of differentiation at work in a somatic practice. It explores rhythmic qualities - flowing, staccato, chaos, lyrical, and stillness - to distinguish and integrate life experiences and aspects of self by dancing these rhythms. Roth's work emphasizes the distinct qualities of each rhythm through a movement sequence that allows each rhythm to build upon the last until the final integrative experience of the stillness rhythm is reached (Roth, 1997).

Differentiation is also an important aspect of the alchemical learning process. Across cultures, alchemical theory describes the birth of the cosmos as a process of differentiation. Much of practical alchemy centers on the separation of matter into its essential components as a way to purify and transform it (Reid, 1998). Medieval inner alchemists engaged in esoteric differentiation called this the *separatio*, and it involved the differentiation of spirit and matter. According to Marie-Louise von Franz, this differentiation precedes the integrative reanimation stage (1980). Taoist theory presents a similar metaphysical understanding of the process of differentiation, and described the universe as engaged in the differentiation and integration of yin and yang.

## Interaction

The interaction of elements or aspects of experience can be thought of as the next step after differentiation and preceding integration. It requires differentiation, in that these qualities must be differentiated first in order to exist in our awareness as separate entities, and it prepares the way for integration. Interaction allows us to contrast and compare the elements we have distinguished through the process of differentiation. By experiencing the differences and similarities between elements, we develop an enhanced understanding of their nature that is not available to us through examination of these elements in isolation. We also begin to experience how differentiated elements work together, paving the way for the possibility of their eventual coordination and integration.

The interaction of elements also generates rhythm and pattern, which is essential to organizing and understanding the relationships between the differentiated aspects of experience (Bender, 1998). Interaction creates rhythm through contrast. It is the repeated changes in quality throughout a sequence of interaction that gives the sequence its rhythmic pattern. This is clearest when the qualities are polarized. For example, muscular activity can be differentiated into two simple polarities - contraction and release. (Think of squeezing your hand into a fist and letting it go.) When these two contrasting movements are repeated, a simple rhythm is created. Adding other movement qualities or parts of the body complexifies the rhythmic pattern, and allows us to experience different ways of organizing these elements.

## Integration

As in many alchemical and somatic processes, the integration of differentiated elements - whether those elements are yin and yang, arms and legs, or body, mind, and spirit - is the next stage in the process of Somatic Alchemy . Both alchemy and somatics emphasize integration, and many of their practices are ultimately devoted to it, whether it is the alchemical integration of the four Elements (MacLean, 1999), the Functional Integration of the Feldenkrais Method®, or the sensory integration work of Jean Ayres (Knaster, 1996).

Integration allows the differentiated aspects of experience to work together for the mutual benefit of the whole. By connecting elements and coordinating efforts, integration allows specialized elements to do their particular job without interference, while still benefiting from the efforts of the team. It allows similar elements to augment the capacities and qualities of the others, and to pool their resources toward a single purpose. It allows for different combinations and permutations of elements, and an increased range of choices in experience and behavior. Integration is not the same as fusion - it is not the indiscriminate melding of distinct elements into a static homogeneous mass. Rather, it holds the paradox of diversity and community within it, and changes as the components that create it change.

## Contextualization

This last stage in the process of Somatic Alchemy refers to the shift in perception that often occurs after integration, when it is noticed that the newly integrated whole is also a differentiated element of a larger whole. As the human hand is an integrated whole requiring the co-ordinated effort of its fingers, so is the hand connected to the larger whole of the arm, which in turn is part of the body. The gestalt[7] of the hand is both a microcosm and a macrocosm, containing and contained within other gestalts. This stage requires us to consider context, and offers an important perspective on each of the stages preceding it. None of the processes of change occur in isolation, and differentiation, interaction, and integration exist on many levels of understanding and experience.

---

[7] Gestalt is a German word roughly translated as a "unified pattern".

## 5.  The results of this research, and their interpretation, are unique to each soma.

The somatic privileging of subjective experience significantly impacts every stage of the research process of Somatic Alchemy   in a way uncommon to many other forms of research.  In contrast with traditional scientific research, somatic research is intended primarily to generate new awareness and choice.  It is a starting point from which to explore somatic experience, rather than an end point that conclusively proves or disproves a particular belief or idea about somatic experience. Because of this shift in emphasis, the analysis and evaluation of somatic research requires a unique set of values.  Traditional forms of empirical study value objective analysis, external validation, and generalizable conclusions.  Somatic research emphasizes the subjective nature of the research data, and recognizes the importance of articulating the unique perspective of the researcher/participant.  All somas are unique, and the research results will reflect these individual variations in experience.

In evaluating the results of somatic research, the complexity of the soma is honored, and multicausal interdependent factors are often more useful in explaining change than single isolated factors.  The criteria of the research's validity is based on completeness, illustrativeness, understanding, and the responsiveness to the researcher/participant's experience.  Lastly, the importance of process as well as product is recognized, and the research process itself is evaluated for its positive contribution to the researcher/participant.

## 6.  All somas are interconnected.

Having just asserted that all somas are unique, and that therefore the results of the research in which Somatic Alchemy is engaged are not generalizable beyond the experience of the researcher/participant, a significant exception or modification to this statement needs to be elaborated.  Despite our distinct individuality, we are also simultaneously connected and related.

We are imbedded in our environments, and share essential features and experiences with them.

Although our somatic experience and movement behavior are the unique to us, we share important commonalities with other members of our gender, culture, and species. In the same way that we are clearly identifiable as individuals not only by our bodily structure but by our bodily behavior (how we laugh, how we walk, our facial expressions), we are recognizable as human, mammalian, vertebrate, etc. by the same measures. As humans, we share a range of types of experience - breathing, sleeping, walking, eating - regardless of our particular life experiences. These common experiences are based in phylogenetic knowing, evolutionary knowledge acquired over the course of the development of the species. Composed of countless sensory-motor programs, phylogenetic knowledge is reflexive and autonomic (Hanna, 1970). We come programmed with this knowledge at birth, and do not need to be taught how to breathe, suckle, or sleep. By enhancing our somatic awareness, we reconnect with the phylogenetic knowledge we share with other human beings.

We are also imbedded in the context of the material world, and our changing understanding of that world offers a glimpse into the nature of physical existence. Research into quantum mechanics shows that material phenomena can appear as both particles and waves. As matter, we humans are both self-contained particles and diffuse, interconnected waves, depending on the experimental situation (Greene, 1997). Alchemists understood our dual nature as both spirit (energy) and matter, and recognized our interconnectedness by envisioning all things as sharing the same Elementary building materials. For thousands of years they have been saying what modern physics now tells us - we are all made of the same stuff, and that stuff is spirit.

# Conclusion

Somatics and alchemy share another crucial understanding in addition to the principles and processes discussed above. Although difficult to define precisely, its impact on the process and structure of Somatic Alchemy outweighs all other considerations, concepts, or perspectives. Modern practical alchemist John Reid speaks to this basic understanding when he emphasizes the difference between the creation of a spagyric[8] product and an alchemical one (Reid, 1998). According to Reid, the spagyric art does not require the spark of life in order to create - the skilled separation, purification, and recombination of ingredients will result in a perfectly acceptable medicine. In order to create a *living* medicine, however, the alchemical artist must capture the spark of life in her work. This distinction may be compared to the one between ordinary physical exercise and somatic movement. Skilled execution of a comprehensive program of physical exercise will likely result in a perfectly acceptable body, perhaps even an exceptional one. It will not, however, result in a poetic body[9]. By staying connected to the somatic encounter of the living body in relation to itself and its environment, Somatic Alchemy seeks to embody the poetic dimension of human experience. Joseph Campbell once said that we are not looking for the meaning of life, but for *the experience of being alive* (Campbell, 1996). It is the possibility of connecting with this elusive but essential life spark that lies at the heart of Somatic Alchemy .

> Re-examine all you have been told at church or school or in any book, dismiss whatever insults your own soul, and your very flesh shall be a great poem and have the richest fluency not only in its words but in the silent lines of its lips and face and between the lashes of your eyes and in every motion and joint of your body.

---

[8] Spagyric refers to a particular technique of working with matter, consisting of separating components, purifying them individually, and recombining them. Spagyrics is often employed in relation to herbal medicine, using the process described above to draw out and magnify a plant's inherent healing properties (Parri, 1999).

[9] In *Care of the Soul*, Thomas Moore describes the "poetic body" as the soul presented in its richest and most expressive form (1992).

*- Walt Whitman, from his preface to the 1855 edition of Leaves of Grass*

# Elemental Movement

# Introduction

> *Movement is the great law of life. Everything moves. The heavens move, the earth turns, the great tides mount the beaches of the world. The clouds march slowly across the sky, driven by a wind that stirs the trees into a dance of branches. Water, rising in the mountain springs, runs down the slopes to join the current of the river. Fire, begun in the brush, leaps roaring over the ground. And the Earth, so slow, so always there, grumbles and groans and shifts in the sleep of the centuries.*

- Mary Whitehouse (*The Tao of the Body*, 1958)

## Moving Inquiries

Elemental Movement is a form of movement education that applies the principles of Somatic Alchemy toward a conscious process of learning and change. It is composed of a series of movement structures -- some formal, and some improvisational -- designed to explore and express the qualities embodied by the five alchemical Elements. Applying the idea of the soma as a laboratory (outlined in the previous chapter), Elemental Movement offers a method for researching the nature of the soma, and, by extension, the nature of the environment in which the soma is interactively embedded. Specifically, the goal of Elemental Movement is to reveal vividly and accurately how the Elements are embodied in each individual soma. The components of an Elemental Movement session are steps in a research project, and every movement structure is an experiment. These movement experiments, like all somatic research, depend upon feedback from the soma for their data (Johnson, 1995) and each one is designed to pursue a specific line of somatic inquiry.

These movement experiments are created specifically to elicit stimuli that act as catalysts for awareness. These catalysts are grounded in phylogenetic knowledge. For example, our common behavioral matrix allows us to make an educated guess that something is very likely to happen somatically when two people dramatically increase their proximity to one another. Based on genetically-inherited somatic intelligence, we can even make educated guesses about the nature of reaction the catalyst will provoke. In the example above, most people will probably experience an increase in somatic arousal, as well as other changes resulting from that increased energy. Because all somas are unique, however, it is impossible to predict exactly what the specific individual reaction to these catalysts will be. This makes the movement experiments dependable (in that something is highly likely to happen) as well as interesting (in that the conclusions are never foregone).

## Elemental Catalysts

The experiments employed in Elemental Movement are based on a particular set of catalysts. Earth, Water, Air, Fire, and Ether can be thought of as the activating agent in a bio-psycho-social reaction where the reagent is your soma. Clearly, the nature of the catalysts is crucial to the process of change, and the Elements were chosen for their unique properties. In selecting a set of symbolic tools for a practice based on the concepts of Somatic Alchemy , it was important to me that the symbols supported diversity along the lines of gender, race, and culture. For example, as a feminist, I am sensitive to the potentially negative impact of working with gender-specific models. Historically, women have been expected to accept a male figure as the designated standard for humanity, and simultaneously discouraged from emulating that ideal (Miller, 1976). Conversely, choosing female-identified archetypes as symbols could limit the capacity of men to identify key aspects of their personhood. Despite the fact that androgyny is an important symbolic device in the practice of alchemy (Jung, 1953), significant dimensions of homosexuality, bisexuality, and transgendering do not seem to be fully addressed by it.

71

Issues around race, age, and class struck me as being equally entangled in, yet generally unresolved by, the use of anthropomorphic symbols. Using natural but non-human symbols was a way to allow a greater diversity of individuals access to meaningful connection. The five Elements also offered a set of symbols whose meanings reached across many of the specifics of culture and era. Because the Elements still resonate in the modern mind despite their antiquity, they seemed ideally suited to the task of reclaiming and revivifying a common mythic heritage. On a personal note, a desire to reclaim my own ancestral roots also played a part in choosing the Elements as the basis of my movement work. Much of my ethnic heritage can be traced back to the Celts, and the centrality of the Elements in pagan Celtic mythology drew me to explore them further, and to incorporate them into my life in a personal, meaningful way.

Another reasoning underlies choosing the Elements from many other possible alchemical symbols. From my perspective, human beings already suffer from an unhealthy degree of self-interest. Our position as dominant species on the planet has not been accomplished with much sensitivity or regard for the larger ecosystem in which we live. In advocating a practice that requires and encourages self-reflection, I did not want to inadvertently add to the already massive focus on our own species. We humans are not the center of the universe, and we would likely exist more happily in it if we paid more attention to forming meaningful and respectful relationships with aspects of the environment outside the narrow scope of our own immediate human concerns. Choosing symbols from Nature that are distinctly not human was one way to invite that expansion of awareness.

## Engaging in the Practice

In offering a description of what Elemental Movement is, it is important to also describe what it is not. Although designed as an inclusive and integrative model, Elemental Movement contains inherent limitations in scope and application. It is intended primarily as a practice for the development of enhanced somatic awareness, and not as an alternative to comprehensive physical exercise, psychotherapy, or spiritual instruction. Individuals with a limited capacity to engage in physical movement, symbolic activity, or sustained periods of perceptual attentiveness will need to adapt the practice to accommodate their abilities and preferences.

The idea of adapting Elemental Movement is actually central to understanding its practice. Every practitioner of the method will need to adapt it, not just the few whose particular requirements fall outside the assumptions of what constitutes "normal." Each soma is unique, and the needs of each individual will reflect that. Because Elemental Movement is a form of somatic research, this approach sets no norms, goals, or expectations in terms of process or results. What is does is pose a set of questions, and offer some suggestions as to how to begin to find your own answers to them. It is important, therefore, that each individual practitioner have the resources available to them to safely and effectively design their own process. For some, that will mean working with an experienced facilitator[10] who can act as an initial guide to the practice. This would likely include individuals engaged in an active process of healing or recovery (from trauma, addiction, illness, or injury, for example) or those whose orientation to consensual reality is easily disrupted[11]. For others, especially those with some previous experience with conscious personal development, this manuscript alone may suffice as a primer.

Elemental Movement shares some definite affinities with other movement practices, as well as possessing unique distinctions. Although grounded in its own specific theoretical framework, many of the movement experiments are inspired by and adapted from other disciplines. The overall structure of the movement sessions is based on my experience as a fitness

---

[10] Because Elemental Movement is an integrative model, facilitators of the approach need to be well-versed in several disciplines. Training and experience in somatic psychotherapy, movement therapy and education, and the expressive arts serve as a foundation for additional training in the theory and practice of Elemental Movement itself.

[11] Elemental Movement is contraindicated for individuals in active crisis or in the acute stages of either physical or mental illness or injury.

instructor and my training in Gestalt therapy. Several of the improvisational and interactive movement structures are compatible with other psychotherapeutic approaches, especially the creative and expressive arts therapies. In contrast, the somatic reflections are largely influenced by somatic education approaches such as Sensory Awareness, Ideokinesis, and Experiential Anatomy. To my knowledge, Elemental Movement is one of few movement-centered approaches to integrate both therapeutic and educational instruments with a primarily somatic orientation.

In addition to its uniqueness as an integrative model, Elemental Movement has several distinguishing characteristics that become clearly apparent in its practice. The first, and most central, is the use of the Elements as the basis for the movement experiments. Their power as archetypal symbols and as transitional objects pervades the practice of Elemental Movement to the extent that practitioners often describe their experience in terms of the relationships they form with the Elements. The experiential dialogue that develops with each Element crosses traditional boundaries between body and mind, as practitioners explore both the concrete and imaginal aspects of the Element. As these qualities become distinguished and clarified, the practitioner is able to integrate them into their experience of themselves.

Another characteristic of Elemental Movement that distinguishes it from most other forms of therapy and education is less immediately obvious, but equally important. The alchemical process upon which Elemental Movement is based has its roots in ancient practices with strong spiritual and philosophical underpinnings. Aspects of various mystical practices[12] are embedded in Elemental Movement , and the spiritual dimensions of this work are always available for those who wish to draw upon them. When medieval alchemists undertook the task of separating and integrating the Elements, they considered it sacred work. Whether we modern practitioners of Elemental Movement consider our own work as sacred is up to us.

---

[12] In this context, *mystical practices* refers to experiential methods for establishing a direct relationship with the sacred, which may or may not be affiliated with an established religion.

The section that follows walks through each of the five steps in an Elemental Movement    session, describing the structure and purpose of each step.  It offers a glimpse into the overall structure and process of Elemental Movement    before proceeding to the actual movement experiments found in the next chapter.


## Understanding the Structure

Elemental Movement    sessions are composed of a series of 5 interconnected steps -

1.   somatic reflection
2.   body/mind activation
3.   expressive movement improvisation
4.   interactive or collective movement structure
5.   distillation/integration

The structure of an Elemental Movement    session follows the basic tenets and meta-process of Somatic Alchemy  .  The first step takes the form of a somatic reflection, and allows us to check in with ourselves to assess the current state of our body of knowledge.  From this initial place of awareness, the steps that follow offer their own possibilities for embodied learning.  The activation step often follows a loose structure designed to offer full range-of-motion movements and opportunities to expand our movement repertoire.  By engaging in a wide range of movement, we learn more about what our bodies can and cannot do, and the many different ways of engaging in the same motion.  From there, movement improvisation allows us to build on our current movement skills by exploring our potential for movement from the spontaneous, creative place of intuition and imagination.  This knowledge is then expanded into the relational dimension through interactive and collective movement structures.  More formally shaped than the improvisation, these structures are ways to engage in new learning about various facets of relationship.  Issues such as boundaries, non-verbal communication, and kinesthetic empathy can be explored. Lastly, the processing step is designed to help us integrate our movement experiences, and generalize the knowledge we have acquired.

Creating a safe process is always a primary concern, and the ordering of the steps is informed by knowledge of basic physiological and psychological processes. For example, the sessions always begin with a somatic reflection to allow us to slowly and gently reconnect with our kinesthetic awareness before engaging in movement activities. For the same reason, the interactive movement structures follow, rather than precede, the individual movement improvisations - our attempts to connect with others are often more effective when we are first connected to our own experience. Warm-up and cool-down components are built into the structure of the sessions, and because the somatic approach emphasizes body/mind integration, these components include warm-up and cool-down activities for both body and mind. Elemental Movement sessions are concluded by processing our movement experiences as a way to begin to integrate them. Although most of these experiences will not be fully integrated by the end of the session, the opportunity to identify them for ourselves offers some sense of closure. Each of the five steps has an important place within the sequence, and draws upon somatic principles to help safeguard our emotional and physical well-being as we move.

These five steps also follow the same ordering of the Elements found in ancient Western alchemical processes - beginning with the heaviest, or most material Element of Earth, and ending with Ether, the lightest, most celestial of Elements. The five Elements lend their particular qualities to each step, regardless of the Element being worked with in the overall process. Thus, a Fire session will explore Fire through five steps - a Fire meditation, a Fire activation, a Fire movement improvisation, etc. - yet each of these steps will be subtly influenced by a different Element. In this way, we begin to distinguish the shades and nuances of each element - the earthy aspects of Water, or the fiery aspects of Air.

For instance, the somatic reflection section is usually performed lying on the floor, and serves the purpose of allowing us to get "grounded" before we begin moving. This is our Earth step even when the entire Elemental Movement session is dedicated to another Element, such as Fire or Water. The activation section is always shaped by Water, as fluid movements provide the safest warm-up for our joints and muscles. Air provides the inspiration for the movement through space often evoked in the expressive movement section. It encourages us to broaden our somatic awareness to the environment around us. The interactive movement structures of the next step involve the exchange of interpersonal energy, and are presided over by the element of Fire. Among other things, Fire represents energy, and it is this exchange of energy that characterizes all relationship, including movement relationships. The distillation and integration phase is influenced by Ether, the invisible Element that permeates and integrates all things. One way to understand the process of integration is to envision it as a form of dispersion and infiltration. It is when a skill or an insight is generalized - i.e. diffused into and available to the whole self - that it can be understood to be truly integrated. The final un-named step in each session involves a return to Earth, completing the cycle and grounding the ethereal. This is often accomplished by sitting on the floor while processing your experience and returning your somatic awareness to the ground for a moment before rising.

Now that the overall process of Elemental Movement has been outlined, the individual steps can be described in more detail. Before proceeding to the first step - Somatic reflection - a section on Creating Elemental Environments is offered as a preface. This section discusses the importance of the holding environment on transformative experience, and describes ways to enhance the safety and energetic ambiance of your working space.

## Creating Elemental Environments

The actual first step in any Elemental Movement session begins before the beginning. If you are participating in a session facilitated by someone else, many of these preparatory steps will be taken for you. If, however, you are designing your own session, it is important to attend to the environment in which you plan to move before beginning the actual practice. It needs to provide a real sense of both physical and emotional safety, encourage freedom of expression, and offer a source of creative inspiration. Creating an environment that supports the work you are about to undertake is crucial to its success.

Some of the basic environmental considerations are commonsense - is the floor clean and free of debris, is there enough room to move, do you have a source of fresh air, enough heat, adequate light? Is there access to water? Is there privacy? Be aware of the size of the space you work in - too large a space can feel intimidating, or can dissipate your sense of energy. Too small a space may limit your expressiveness, or distract your focus too often towards avoiding obstructions.

Once the practical considerations are taken care of, you can begin to create an atmosphere that will enhance your explorations. Often, the first task in creating a supportive environment is to claim the space. Before you begin the session, take a walk around the whole space to get yourself oriented - touch the walls and floor, look out the window, take a big breath of air, listen to the ambient background noise, locate the space in its larger context in your mind's eye. Sometimes bringing a personal object into the center of the space acts to signal that this space is yours. Another way to claim space is to walk around the perimeter as if to enclose it with the path of your movement. Everything inside the enclosure is yours.

Once the environment is safe and secured, you can attend to enriching it. One way to think of inspirational ambiance is to work with the senses - especially sight, hearing, and smell. For example, if you wanted to enhance the ambiance for a Fire session, you might consider placing a reddish-tinted screen in front of your main light source to bathe the room in a warm, fiery glow. A spice or wood-based incense and background soundtrack of a crackling fire could also help create an environment that inspires your exploration of the Element of Fire. For me, the right music is crucial to setting the tone of the work and for providing a sensory base of inspiration. I use "ambient" music - often soundtracks of nature sounds - as well as classical, jazz, folk, and popular music.

The discography at the end of this manuscript offers some ideas for "ambient" musical accompaniment as well as musical selections for each of the five Elements. Use the music you love, and don't worry if it doesn't fit clearly into a particular Elemental category. Like everything else, music is a place where all the Elements intermingle.

Symbolic objects evocative of the Elements can also play a role in creating the right environment, as do movement instruments. You might choose to create a collection of objects that remind you of the Elements and place them randomly in the space so they catch your eye as you move. Or you can create an Elemental altar to place in the center of your moving space. I use an earthenware bowl of stones, a blue bowl of water, a candle, and a feather as my Elemental objects, and arrange them in alignment with the cardinal directions. (According to Wiccan tradition, the Earth object sits in the northern position, Water in the West, Air in the East, and Fire in the South.) Movement instruments serve both as symbolic manifestations and as a way to shape our movements in particular ways - a blue silk scarf becomes a watery stream lying draped along the floor, and in our arms it guides us to move in continuous flowing arcs. Sometimes I use balloons to evoke Airy movement responses. A stone serves as a visual token of the Earth, and when we dance with it, its weight pulls our movements into the Earthly bounds of gravity. Other times I will use small tree branches as Earth symbols - they also serve as rhythm instruments. Because my mother wisely taught me never to play with matches, I use flashlights or bright red tangles of yarn to evoke the qualities of Fire. The following list contains additional movement tools for expanding your movements, and creating new movement experiments:

- long stretchy bands of fabric (Lycra is good)
- parachutes
- big balloons
- fans
- ribbon sticks
- flags
- elastic ropes

Using costume as part of the Elemental Movement session is another possible source of inspiration, and offers an opportunity to temporarily step out of our daily persona and "try on" a dimension of self outside our normal experience. In creating an Elemental costume, aim for the figurative somatic experience rather than a literal interpretation of the Element. What kind of clothing helps you to feel "ethereal" when you wear it? What evokes your "earthy" temperament? This strategy for eliciting the sensual and symbolic qualities of the Elements need not be limited to Elemental Movement   sessions, and are a wonderful way to bring the Elements into our daily experience.  For example, I remember a phase in my life when wearing black clothing was a deeply-felt comfort to me.  Although others wondered whether I was depressed or trying to make a political fashion statement, I intuitively recognized the need to connect with the transcendent, universal qualities of Ether, and found a symbolic way to achieve that connection through the use of color.  At other times, I have found myself drawn to light, almost weightless clothing, and noticed that the experience of wearing it was a needed breath of fresh Air...

# Elemental Steps

## Step One:  Somatic Reflection

Because many of us experience some degree of disconnection from our kinesthetic perception, any session in Elemental Movement   begins with an opportunity to focus and center our somatic awareness.  The somatic reflection section allows us to slowly and gently reconnect with our body selves before engaging in movement activities.  It is when we are "out of touch" with our bodily experience that we are most likely to get injured, so this step serves a very real physical safety function.  It also provides an opportunity to minimize our risk of emotional or psychological injury - especially when interacting with others, the possibility of getting our feelings hurt is always present to some degree.  By checking in with ourselves before moving, we can assess our emotional state in terms of our readiness to take those risks. If we discover that we're feeling fragile or tired or irritated, we can take steps to take care of ourselves - choosing to move more gently, or to approach others with more care. This is also the time to remember to have your Emotional Safety Kit in good working order (see Table on the following page).

## Emotional Safety Kit

An Emotional Safety Kit is a figurative term referring to a set of skills that can help you in managing the emotional responses to certain experiences. Our somas possess an extraordinary capacity for sensation, and eliciting new somatic responses can sometimes be experienced as unpleasant or overwhelming. Although we cannot always be assured that the somatic experiences we generate though Elemental Movement are universally positive ones, we can take steps to minimize any distress that may accompany them. The Emotional Safety Kit offers some strategies for dealing with troublesome feelings in the context of an Elemental Movement session.

### Stop
Sometimes a sensation can be perceived as unsettling simply because it is unknown; other times the feelings are inherently painful, or evoke anger, sadness, or fear. Whatever the case, the most sensible strategy is to stop whatever activity is producing the sensations, and attend to minimizing its impact. After stopping the eliciting activity, the process for managing unwanted emotional responses can be summed up as one of grounding, orienting, comforting, and bracketing:

### Ground
Alarm is a natural response to distress of any kind. Grounding counters our soma's instinctive flight response, so that we can focus on resolving the discomfort. Grounding involves getting physically close and connected to the ground - sit if you are standing, and put both feet fully on the floor. Take a nice, slow, easy breath.

### Orient
Once you're grounded, create some breathing space from the (usually internal) source of distress by focusing on the present external environment[1]. Look slowly and deliberately around the room. Name what you see (aloud if it helps). Listen to the sounds inside and outside the room. Reach down and touch the floor, and notice the texture. Make eye contact with someone you feel safe with. By emphasizing the perceptual reliability of the here-and-now setting, we reassure ourselves that the world is still here despite our personal upset. Because the emotional discomfort most likely to emerge during a somatic experiment will be something connected to the past, orienting to the environment also helps anchor us back in the present.

**Comfort**

Now that we have created some space between the upsetting feelings and present awareness, offering ourselves some comfort often helps to dissipate any remaining troubled energy. Find a place on your body that it might feel good to offer the physical touch of your own hand. This might be the place where the distress was experienced, or somewhere else that feels comforting to hold - perhaps your belly, chest, or feet. Continue to take slow easy breaths, and offer yourself some words of comfort. Lean up against something solid, curl up in something soft, wrap yourself in something warm (but don't lose your orientation to the external environment...). Other people can also be a wonderful source of comfort, if that feels right for you. Being able to talk about your experience can often help settle upset feelings.

**Bracket**

Sometimes the emotional distress we experience as a result of somatic exploration is indicative of a deeper unresolved problem or issue in our lives. When this is the case, we can be torn between wanting to work on the issue and needing to take care of ourselves in the moment. Bracketing allows us to safely put away our feelings until we are able to address them more fully. Bracketing involves a) acknowledging the feeling, b) containing it by placing it in your mind's eye behind a wall, in a box, or between two imaginary parentheses, and c) putting it away with the promise that you will retrieve it when you are in a better position to address it. Keeping your internal agreement to address the issue at a later date is crucial to the long-term success of this strategy, so make sure the agreement is both specific and reasonable. Bracketing is also useful when material emerges that relates to ongoing work you are addressing elsewhere - in therapy, for example.

Not only does attending to our somatic awareness prepare us - physically and emotionally - for the activities to come, it serves as our primary method of observation in the somatic research process. By attending to our somatic experience before we begin to move, we allow ourselves to take a somatic reading of our current internal state. This "check-in" gives us a point of comparison from which to discern any changes resulting from our subsequent movement experiences. It is the primary pre-test measure in our somatic research.

This first step is also used as a form of somatic education, and includes an experiential exploration of anatomical, physiological or kinesiological principles. Drawing on the work of

Mabel Todd, Bonnie Bainbridge Cohen, Caryn McHose, Andrea Olsen, and Irmgard Bartenieff, these experiments use the Elements as the basis for exploring different parts, systems, and functions of the soma. For example, a somatic reflection for the Earth Element might explore our somatic relationship to gravity, where an Air meditation might focus on the breath.

## Step Two:  Activation

The activation step builds on the somatic awareness introduced in the meditation, and serves many of the same purposes. It continues the process of waking up the soma, orienting us to our environments (both internal and external), and assessing conditions that need to be attended to in order to move safely and fully into the movement experiences to come. It serves as a warm-up for the soma, in the same way that stretching and limbering exercises serve to warm up our muscles before a run.

The activation process occurs on three basic levels, each dealing with our relationship to a particular environment. Warming up the somatic environment involves experiments to activate sensory perceptions - especially touch, sight, and hearing. Attending to our sensory instruments allows us to ensure they are tuned up and turned on. This stage also includes a loosely structured series of easy, slow movements in the full range of motion to help prepare the heart, lungs, joints, and muscles for more intensive and sustained movement. Warming-up the body involves a general warm-up to raise pulse and body temperature, as well as a task-oriented warm-up that targets the specific muscles used in the activities that follow. A thorough warm-up has both physical and psychological benefits, according to Ileana Pina, director of cardiac rehabilitation at Temple University in Philadelphia (A Better Warm-Up, *Allure*, 1993). Not only does a proper warm-up allow muscles to access oxygen more efficiently, contract more forcefully, and transmit nerve impulses more quickly, it also improves concentration and self-assurance.

Warming up to the physical environment involves a process of gradually exploring and claiming space in the room. We are in a constant process of adapting to our external surroundings, and making this adaptation more conscious allows us a fuller range of choices in how we interact with them. ("Should I ask if we can open a window? Move that chair? Turn down the heat?") This warm-up step reiterates some of the same themes addressed during the stage of preparing the environment discussed earlier, and allows the co-researchers in a facilitated Elemental Movement   session to create a sense of safe space and holding environment for themselves.

Warming the social environment means attending to our relationships with the other people we will be moving with - making contact, saying hello, and noticing our somatic response to the presence of others as we slowly increase our attention to and interaction with them. The movement experiments used in this stage of the activation step are inspired by several sources. The sociometric techniques developed by J.L. Moreno, founder of psychodrama, offer a set of action tools for uncovering the invisible webs of interpersonal connection which comprise our social environment. Dance therapy and Gestalt therapy also employ a range of non-verbal exercises designed specifically for group warm-up. These techniques served as the impetus for the design of the somatic experiments used in Elemental Movement to acclimatize movers to the social environment.

One way to assess the overall effectiveness of the activation step is to view the process in relation to breathing. With respect to the breath, the meditation step offers us an opportunity to check to see if we are able to continue to "breathe easy" while in conscious contact with our own bodies. The activation step allows us to test this ability with respect to movement - "Can I move and still breathe?" - as well as in relation to space - "Can I breathe and be aware of being in the room?" - and to people - "What happens to my breathing when I notice others?" The awareness that you are subtly "holding" your breath with respect to any of these environments is usually an indicator that you are not sufficiently warmed up. Rather than push past any discomfort at this stage, linger a little longer at this step to see if you can take care of whatever is inhibiting the free and easy flow of your breath.

## Step Three: Expressive Movement

Of all the steps in Elemental Movement , the expressive movement improvisations probably share the strongest affinity with dance[13]. They are usually supported by a particular piece or style of music, and often display an inherent sense of rhythm and pattern. In contrast to most dance, however, these improvisations do not have any formal steps and are not performed with any audience in mind. They are created in the moment by the movers themselves, for the sole purpose of generating somatic experience. In *Moment of Movement*, Lynne Anne Blom and L. Tarin Chaplin (1988) describe improvisation as fusing creation with execution, with the dancer simultaneously originating and performing movement without preplanning. It is free association[14] in motion, tapping into the unconscious and allowing the free and spontaneous expression of personal material - ideas, images, emotions, and impulses.

Using the Elements as inspiration, the expressive movement improvisations allow an opportunity to move "as if" one were Earth, or Water, or Fire. By "embodying" the Element in this way, it is possible to have a direct experience of some of the qualities and properties of the Element. Creating an accurate or objective representation of the Element is not the purpose here. Rather, the experiment is based on the idea that our imaginations will naturally be drawn to perceiving, creating, and expressing those qualities which are most relevant for us in the moment. Other times, the movement emerges in somatic response to an imagined encounter with an Element, and the improvisation becomes a kind of duet. This process of blending imagination with movement grounded in kinesthetic sensation is inherently creative, and often deeply compelling to watch as well as to experience. Gail Gustafson (1999), a somatically-oriented

---

[13] The Mirriam-Webster Dictionary defines *movement* as the act or process of changing place, position, or posture, and *dance* as a series of rhythmic and patterned bodily movements usually performed to music.

[14] Free association is a psychoanalytic technique in which the analysand (client) is encouraged to freely verbalize whatever thoughts come to mind without censoring, editing, or planning.

choreographer and teacher of the performing arts, describes dancers trained in somatic awareness as possessing a "wholeness" that makes them stand out.

Expressive movement improvisation can be exhilarating as well as gratifying, and it is easy to be swept away by the moment. Surrendering to the joy of moving needs to be balanced by safety, however. The somatic awareness awakened in the first two steps is put into active practice in the improvisation section, as the best way to ensure your movements do not harm your body is to stay in conscious contact with it. The movement elicited in these improvisations can also become cardiovascularly demanding, and it is essential that this section be interspersed with effort monitoring, and followed by stretches and a cardiovascular cool-down. Effort monitoring is an alternative to checking the pulse for an indicator of cardiovascular exertion. A good basic guideline for movement improvisations is that you should never become so out of breath that you are unable to carry on a verbal conversation. If you find yourself becoming tired or winded, but still want to continue to move with the same quality of energy as before, find smaller movements that express the same kind of feeling. Instead of moving all the parts of your body, move just one part while remaining engaged and connected to your whole body. For example, you can continue to move very fiercely with much less effort if you scale your movements down to just your hands.

After your movement improv is complete, it is important to keep moving quietly and gently for a couple of minutes as a way to let your cardiovascular system slowly cool down. Keep moving until your breathing has settled back to nearly normal, and your body temperature is comfortable. This is also a good time to have a drink of water. Complete your cool-down by stretching out all the muscles you worked in your movement improv. Stretching brings oxygenated blood into the muscles, and helps remove the excess lactic acid that can cause stiffness later. A good basic set of stretches is offered in Appendix One.

The expressive movement improvisations in Elemental Movement can generate a rich stream of images, ideas, emotions, and sensations. (If your find yourself struggling to cope with the intensity of this material, remember to use the strategies in the Emotional Safety Kit section.) Given its richness and complexity, you may wish to continue to work with this Elemental material in other artistic mediums as a way to develop it further. Write a poem, sing a song, draw a picture, or create a sculpture. You can also blend modalities - singing and moving in unison, or painting directly onto a surface with different body parts as you move. Some ideas for intermodal expressive improvs are described in the Embodied Elements section under each Element.

## Step Four: Interactive and Collective Movement

Up until now, the practice of Elemental Movement has been discussed as though it were primarily a solitary pursuit. Privileging internal felt awareness does not negate the significance of the interpersonal environment, however, and this step takes somatic experience into the relational dimension. In the previous steps of the Elemental Movement process, our primary task has been to focus our attention on the inner level of kinesthetic reality - to listen deeply within. In this step, our task is to broaden the range of our attentiveness so that we are able to listen to the kinesthetic reality of others as it manifests in their movement, breath, gesture, and expression. These interactive and collective movement structure offers an opportunity to experiment with how our somas are affected by interactions with other somas, and to distinguish the diversity and commonalities of somatic experience.

The interactive movement structures focus on moving with others in a way that creates a movement dialogue with them. Often carried out in dyads, these experiments focus on a particular topic related to an Element. For example, the rhythm experiments of the expressive movement improvs in the Earth session explore how our internal rhythms can be expressed externally with our own movements. The interactive movement structures expand on this theme, and involve building a rhythmic conversation with other movers. This exchange involves both "listening" and "speaking" in movement, and often follows a back-and-forth pattern. How we engage in these movement dialogues can illuminate the larger dimensions of our relational style, and the simple but concrete structures allow us to experiment with new ways of interacting with others. Moving with a partner also offers the experience of witnessing and be witnessed by another[15]. Seeing our own somatic experience echoed and understood in someone else's body, while simultaneously recognizing their movements as unique, allows us to make the comparisons that eventually relate our microcosmic somatic experience to the macrocosm.

In contrast to a dialogue of individual voices, the collective movement structures more closely resemble a movement choir. These movement experiments are usually conducted in unison, with each mover bringing their own movements into some sort of organized harmony with others. Collective movement structures build on the phylogenetic commonality of somatic experience, and allow us to explore an often deeply-felt source of connection with others. Elemental Movement uses the Elements as the basis of that connection. When the movements of each member of the group reflect the same Elemental quality, the kinesthetic and emotional relationship is enhanced. The relational significance of unison movement forms the psychological cornerstone of many community spiritual and religious practices, including Shaker dancing, and is discussed at more length in the Collective Movement Structures of the Ether section.

In both the interactive and collective movement structures, the experiments are designed with a higher degree of structure than the expressive movement improvisations. Clear, definite steps and guidelines for conducting the experiment ensures that everyone is on the same page, and prevents movers from unwittingly working at cross-purposes. For some, the interactive and collective movement structures present a challenge to staying connected to their own kinesthetic awareness. They experience a tendency to lose felt contact with themselves when attending to another person; conversely, they find it difficult staying connected to others while in full possession of their own somatic experience. These boundary issues are ideally suited to exploration through

---

[15] Janet Adler (1987) describes the significance of being seen as deeply rooted, and related to our longing to be known and understood by others.

movement, as the relationship between physical and process boundaries is clarified[16].

## Step Five: Distillation and Integration

The final step in the Elemental Movement    experience is designed to distill the results of the somatic experiments conducted in the previous steps. It allows us to process and integrate what we have discovered about our somas, so that we can apply this learning to other areas of our life. Extracting insight and meaning from somatic experiences is not the same as analyzing and interpreting them. The process is organic, more like digestion than dissection. As we allow the experience to move through us, we apply the digestive "enzymes" of our own curiosity, observe how it transforms itself, and open ourselves to absorb the nutrients it offers. Although this process is more a matter of allowing than doing, there are still many ways in which we can facilitate it. Conversely, it is helpful to understand some of the ways in which we can hinder the process of distillation and integration (both our own and others), so that they might be avoided.

The most important element of facilitating the distillation of a somatic experience is to remember that the process of integration also needs to be somatic in nature. Although we may be culturally predisposed to attempt to figure out the meaning of a somatic experience by thinking about it, it is much more effective if we allow ourselves to kinesthetically feel our way through it. Remembering the experience kinesthetically allows us to hold the experience authentically while simultaneously bringing the added perspective of heightened consciousness to bear upon it.   The Focusing® work of Eugene Gendlin (1981) offers a simple and effective method of integrating somatic experience, and I

---

[16] Proxemics studies the interpersonal use of space, and how physical boundaries are established and negotiated. Process boundaries refer to the awareness of psychological "space", such as the experience of emotional invasion or abandonment. The experiential relationship between these two types of boundary issues is explored in the Interactive Movement Structure for the Element of Air.

recommend it highly to anyone interested in a comprehensive approach to processing somatic material. The steps outlined below are adapted from that work, as well as from Gestalt therapy techniques.

1. After completing the somatic experiments in an Elemental Movement session, take a moment or two before proceeding to the active processing and integrating step. Integrating learning experiences is natural to us, and it hardly ever serves to push the river. Waiting allows our soma to begin the "digestive" process itself, and allows us to position our conscious awareness in the role of observer/facilitator, not doer/fixer.

2. When you're ready, allow yourself to recreate your somatic experience by remembering how it felt. Rather than immersing yourself fully in that remembered experience, situate your conscious attention at enough distance to be able to experience the kinesthetic memory as well as your current somatic experience. You may discover that other kinesthetic memories also come into your awareness. Make room for them as well, but remain clearly anchored to the present moment as the primary ground of your experience.

3. As you remember each somatic event, ask yourself what you notice about the quality of that experience. Allow the nuances, subtleties, patterns, and affinities of that experience to come into your consciousness. Notice if other sensory phenomena arise in connection with the felt experience. Does the experience have shape or color? If that kinesthetic experience generated an acoustic vibration, what sound would it make? Does this somatic experience remind you of other experiences? Allow all of the associations inherent in the experience to emerge, without manufacturing, emphasizing, or interpreting them. Forced connections created out of the need to impose meaning are rarely useful, and do more to block the integrative process than assist it.

4. Do something to concretize your experience. Write it, draw it, or sculpt it. If expressing your somatic experience outside your body doesn't feel right, then find a word, image, or

sensation that will serve as an internal icon for that experience, and take note of it.

5. Share your experience with someone else. How we choose to describe our experience to another person often reflects the significance we attach to certain elements. Having an experience witnessed by another also allows it the opportunity to solidify in the context of shared reality. Be mindful of how you express your experience, and how your witness responds. (See *Guidelines for Sharing*, on the following page.)

At this point, the somatic experience you originally recreated should be much richer in detail, and many of the hidden meanings may have already emerged. It should also be more definitely located in relation to other experiences you have had. If the experience still feels unsettled, unfinished, or presses for further resolution, try initiating an imaginary dialogue with it. Ask the experience what it needs in order to feel more resolved, or ask what message it has for you. Sometimes the experience feels complete, but still lacks a sense of being sufficiently understood. When this is the case, it may be useful to attend not to the experience itself so much as to our manner of perceiving it. These processing questions inspired by a workshop with Martha Eddy offer some different lenses from which to view experience:

- Observe your remembered experience as though it were being experienced by someone else (i.e., She's remembering a strange fluttering sensation in her stomach, and it worries her. She worries too much about sensations she can't explain...).
- Observe your observations as though they had been made by someone else (i.e., This observer notices the emotional component of somatic experience. They have a tendency to judge, rather than sympathize...).

Although the nature of these questions removes us somewhat from the subjective stance so valued by a somatic perspective, they can be useful in uncovering the particular idiosyncrasies of our own inner observer. Understanding our preferences in viewing experience allows us greater clarity when choosing which information to include and emphasize in the distillation process.

Processing somatic experiences with others can enhance our understanding of ourselves and others, offer invaluable perspective, and underscore our common experience as human beings. Despite these tangible benefits, there are some risks involved in sharing our internal reality with other people. In a desire to be understood, we run the risk of being misunderstood. In wanting to be close, we risk being accidentally invaded or dismissed. These risks can be minimized by following the guidelines on the following page.

## Guidelines for Sharing

### Own Your Experience
- When describing your own somatic experiences, begin your sentences with the pronoun "I". (E.g., "I feel...", " I experience...", "I imagine..."). Using the pronouns "it" or "you" or "we" inaccurately presents a subjective experience as if it were an objective one. Stay connected to your somatic experience as you describe it. Keep your descriptions concrete and specific. If you want to share an abstraction of your experience, name it as such. Do not generalize your experience to others. Listen to your bodily reaction as you speak, and honor your own limits if you feel uncomfortable sharing certain material. It is always easier to add a comment later, than it is to un-say it.

### Listen with Your Body
- When someone is sharing their experience with you, allow your whole soma to respond to what they say. Allow yourself to empathize kinesthetically - for your body to be affected by their words, gestures, expression, and tone of voice. Listening with your body allows essential somatic material to be communicated from one soma to another.

### Respond from Your Own Experience
- Often, the best response to someone relating their somatic experience is a non-verbal one. Make eye contact, face the speaker, and let your facial expressions indicate when you agree or relate to something they have said. Don't interrupt, with words or body language. If you want to respond verbally to someone's material, ask their permission first. In responding, offer only your own somatic experience, using the same guidelines as above (e.g., "When you described..., I felt..."). Try not to offer analysis or abstractions, even of your own experience.

These guidelines for sharing your experiences with others offer a basic set of steps for maximizing the benefits of group interaction in the distillation/integration step of Elemental Movement . With practice, this process can be expanded and refined so that the exchange of somatic material becomes an exciting forum for authentic connection between group members, shared creativity, and interpersonal bonding.

Once the somatic experiences of your Elemental Movement   session have been distilled into essential learnings, you can begin to apply them to your daily life. Although the integration step often occurs outside the setting of the Elemental Movement   session itself, it should not be regarded as an afterthought. On the contrary, this integration step is crucial to the overall process of change being undertaken in Somatic Alchemy   . Unless the knowledge gathered from your movement experiments becomes generalized to the rest of your life, its value is limited to the momentary satisfaction of the session.   Facilitating the integration process ensures that the changes we make in our somatic reality are enduring ones.

Although some generalization of learning takes places naturally without any real effort on our part, we can maximize the effects of this process by bringing our conscious attention to bear. The simplest way to do this is to take note of any insight or awareness produced during an Elemental Movement   session before moving on to other activities. For example, perhaps one session you discovered a particular way of moving that helped your joints feel more lubricated. In the distillation process, you came up with the imaginal icon of an oilcan to help you describe what you learned. Integrating that learning means remembering to take the oilcan with you after you finish the session, and remembering to use it the next time you experience stiff, squeaky hinges.   The final phase of integration occurs when you notice how applying your learning changes your experience.

Another way of integrating the Elemental Movement experience into daily life is to accentuate the Elemental qualities inherent in other activities. For instance, the morning shower can become a daily opportunity to play with the Element of Water. Rather than simply going through the automatic motions of washing up, allow yourself to soak up the unique sensual and kinesthetic qualities of the Element. Stick your arm out the car window on the way to work, and feel the Air whipping around and pressing on your skin. Light a candle at dinner. Go barefoot in your backyard. Look at the night sky more often. Notice how it goes on forever.

# The Embodied Elements

The following chapters describe a series of somatic experiments for each of the five Elements, as well as offering questions to assist in processing and integrating the experiences arising out of those experiments. Before beginning your somatic exploration of the Elements, however, it will be useful to create a map of your current embodied experience of the Elements to provide you with some measure of your progress as you proceed through the material. The following exercise offers one way to assess your initial somatic awareness[17].

## Mapping the Embodied Elements

In many alchemical, philosophical, and mythical traditions, the body - like the cosmos - is composed of five Elements. In this guided imagination exercise, you will be asked to suspend our modern scientific notions of the body and imagine that your body is actually composed of Earth, Water, Air, Fire, and Ether. It's okay if your perceptions are vague or uncertain - just notice what you are aware of. Later you will be asked to describe and illustrate your perceptions and sensations of each Element by filling in an outline of your body on a piece of blank paper.

- Lie in a comfortable position on the floor and breathe easily and deeply. As you breathe, allow the awareness of your breath to bring your attention inwards to the kinesthetic sensations and perceptions of your body. Notice how you feel in your body right now.

---

[17] Please Note: The experiential and exploratory nature of the exercises described in this section may evoke unexpected responses. A relaxed attitude of self-observation may facilitate the integration of these responses into a learning experience. Attempts to classify, analyze, aestheticize, or minimize these responses should be deferred until the new material has had time to emerge fully into awareness. If the material is experienced as overwhelming, grounding, orientation to the present external reality, and the enlistment of a supportive environment are suggested. Please read the Emotional Safety Kit section that describes this process, and practice it before engaging in the exercises.

- When you're ready, begin to imagine how your body holds the Elements. Try to imagine them kinesthetically as well as visually. For each of the Elements in turn, consider the following questions:

Where in your body do you experience this Element? Is it diffused throughout your body or localized? Does the concentration or intensity of this Element vary from one part of your body to the next?

How do you experience the qualities of this Element? Does it have a shape, pattern, speed, color, temperature, direction, sound, sensation, weight, or pressure?

How do you feel emotionally about your experience of this Element in your body? Does it have any memories or associations connected to it for you?

- When you have explored your somatic experience of each of the five Elements, take several full, easy breaths and slowly bring your attention back to your surroundings.
- When you're ready, describe your experience by mapping it on the paper outline of your body. Use color, images, shapes, textures, and words to describe your experience.
- Refer back to your Elemental Body Map throughout your journey through the Elemental Movement process. Add new insights and experiences to it as you go, or create a new map when you have completed the experiments for all the Elements.

# Earth

The Element of Earth is the ground upon which the movement explorations of Elemental Movement are built. It represents the solid, practical, fundamental aspects of this work, and encourages the basic experience of *what is* before we progress to the possibilities of *what could be*. Like the mother that she is, Earth provides the safety, support, and stability we need in order to create confident, dependable movement expressions of who we are. Earth is about feeling solid, centered, and grounded. A secure attachment to Mother Earth gives us a safe place from which to encounter the environment.

On a somatic level, our primary relationship to Earth is based on gravity. Developmentally, this relationship to the earth occurs very early in life, and involves issues of trust. If you don't bond with gravity, you cannot trust you are being supported. You have to hold on. Once you feel bonded to the earth, then you can feel safe to push away (Olsen, 1991). Our somatic orientation to gravity is so essential to our existence that fully 90% of the metabolic energy of the central nervous system is devoted to it (Juhan, 1999). Earth teaches us the letters of the movement alphabet - most of the instinctive reflexes and equilibrium responses that underlie our volitional movement are responses to gravity. When these primary movement patterns are integrated, volitional movement becomes elegant and agile. The somatic reflection experiments that follow explore this fundamental relationship to gravity, and how it affects our somatic experience.

## Somatic Reflections for Earth

### Gravity Connection

(adapted from Andrea Olsen's *Bodystories*)

- Lie belly down on the floor in an X, with arms and legs comfortably extended. As you breathe, release the entire surface of your body into the Earth. (The experience of release is not a passive surrender to gravity, but a willing, active connection with it.) Release your eyes, your mouth, your throat, your breath, your belly, your hips, your arms and legs. Image your center of gravity just in front of your lower back or sacrum (sacrum is Latin for sacred bone). Allow your center of gravity to feel connected to the center of the Earth. Experience the bond you have with gravity, and allow yourself to feel supported by the Earth. Slowly find a way to come to standing while still bonded with the Earth. As you move away from the floor, stay connected to your center of gravity (sacrum) and the shifts in relationship to gravity that it must go through to come to standing.

## Roots and Wings

- With your feet firmly planted on the ground, spread your toes for stability and distribute your weight evenly over both feet. Unlock your knees, and drop the weight of your hips down through your leg muscles. Breathe deeply and imagine a tree, its roots growing down into the earth, spreading deep and wide to provide support. When you feel grounded, allow your spine and neck to lengthen, and your head to float up like a balloon with your spine as the string. Let your back, chest, and shoulders widen like wings. Allow your arms to lengthen from your shoulders and your hands relax. Stand easy and breathe softly and deeply.

## Footwork

Whether walking, standing, or sitting, our feet are the place where our relationship with Earth is most actively experienced. Our feet are highly sensitive and articulate structures, relaying a constant stream of information from the Earth to the rest of the soma. Despite their importance in locomotion, balance, and support, we are often unaware of the somatic experience in our feet. The following ideas are places to begin to reconnect with our feet, and through them to the Earth.

- Stroke, hold, or massage your feet. Use strong, deep, light, quick, smooth and tapping movements. Gently articulate the joints. Trace the arches. Tickle them. Do your hands have a message for your feet? Do your feet have a message for the rest of you?

- Trace the outline of your feet on a piece of drawing paper. Use your imagination and somatic awareness to fill in the outlines.
- Go for a walk while your somatic awareness is focused on the connective relationship between your feet and the floor. Move slowly, and feel how your feet respond to the shifts in weight that walking demands. Imagine you have eyes on the soles of your feet. How does this change how you experience walking?

## Sensory Dimensions of Earth

Although primarily directed at exploring kinesthetic experience, Elemental Movement uses the full range of senses to connect with the Elements. On a sensory level, the element of Earth may evoke a range of sensations and qualities. These sensory responses will vary from one person to the next, and from one session to another. Notice what qualities emerge when you allow yourself to engage in this form of creative imagination.

- When you imagine listening to the Earth, what sounds come to your mind's ear? Sometimes I hear drums and the faint rumblings of an earthquake - deep, resonant sounds. Other times, the quiet chirp of crickets connects me to Earth.
- What colors feel like Earth to you? Is it the rich chocolate of freshly dug soil, the dusty gray of parched hardpan, the pale gold of grain, the deep velvet green of a forest? Imagine one and envelop yourself in it.
- How does Earth smell? Does it evoke memories of fresh green grass, the smell of the sidewalk after a summer rain, or the damp loamy smell of the forest? Take a deep breath of it.
- If I were going to get a taste of Earth, I'd be biting into something savory, full of root vegetables, grains, and mushrooms, seasoned with cumin and Middle Eastern spices. What tastes are Earthy for you?

*Figure 2*

## Elemental Mantra

The Sanskrit letter for the Element of Earth is La. You may use it as part of a mantra-centered meditation by repeating it silently with each breath for a period of 15 or 20 minutes while resting quietly.

## Activating Explorations for Earth

The activation explorations for the Element of Earth are centered on eliciting an experience of the basic ABCs of human movement. On a developmental level, this movement alphabet is composed of the instinctive reflexes and responses that are part of our phylogenetic movement heritage. Both Judith Kestenberg and Bonnie Bainbridge Cohen have worked extensively in the area of developmental movement, and suggestions for exploring their work further are offered in the Resources Section. The following movement experiment offers a brief glimpse into some of the developmental movement patterns available to us.

- Lie comfortably on the floor loosely curled in a semi-fetal position. Breathe slowly and easily. Gradually bring your awareness to your navel. Play with small contracting and expanding movements initiated from your center. Expand these movement to gradually include the rest of your body, and involve full flexion and extension of the spine.
- Find a way to use this flexing movement to initiate locomotion.

A wonderfully articulated and comprehensive set of these basics are offered in the work of movement therapy pioneer Irmgard Bartenieff. Bartinieff Fundamentals® were designed to take the body through a set of kinesthetic events that prepare the mover to access the widest range of effort and spatial shaping possibilities available to them. Through a series of movements, the interplay between different muscle groups in the body is brought into awareness. With such awareness, the possibility then exists of restoring the under-used or mis-used muscles to their appropriate participation. Although perfecting these movement fundamentals takes years of work and expert instruction, the two examples offered here provide a brief introduction. Both are adapted from Bartenieff's *Body Movement: Coping with the Environment* (1980). A movement experiment focused on the simple act of walking completes the activation section.

## Heel Rock

This movement experiment introduces a rhythmic foot movement for the purposes of exploring the connections between the heel, pelvis, spine, and head.

- Lie flat on the floor with your back, legs and arms extended, arms resting at your side.
- Keeping your heels anchored to the floor, point your feet bend downward toward the floor, initiating from the ankle, which retracts the heels and tilts the pelvis slightly forward.
- Reverse the action from the ankle to bring the feet up. This stretches the heels and tilts the pelvis slightly backward.
- Repeat the two foot actions which reverberate into the pelvic area and produce a rhythmical rocking of pelvis and feet.
- It is important that the foot movement is always initiated from the ankle, not the toes, and that no tension occurs in lumbar extensor muscles and surface abdominals, particularly the rectus abdominus. Otherwise the connection between heel and pelvic floor cannot be experienced.

## Arm Circles

This exercise facilitates a clarity of diagonal connection between upper and lower body halves.

- Lie on your back with arms extended at shoulder level, knees bent and feet flat on the floor. Slowly let your knees drop over to the right and let them rest there comfortably. Extend your left arm upward along the floor until it falls into the same diagonal line as your thighs. Notice the gentle pull on your right hip.

- Beginning with your palm up, use your hand to slowly trace a large circle counterclockwise along the floor over your head, and across your body and hips. Pause when your arm has returned to its original position. Allow your eyes to follow your hand as it traces the circle, and notice the rotations your arm moves through to complete the circle. Repeat the movement using a clockwise motion. Then drop your knees to the left, and repeat on that side.

## Earth Walk

This activation experiment combines the injury-prevention benefits of a gradual increase in movement with a guided visualization.

- With both feet planted solidly on the ground, begin to shift your weight from side to side. Swing your arms and walk in place without lifting your feet off the ground - just your heels will lift. Increase the energy of your walk until you find a comfortable rhythm. Allow your walking movement to include your whole body - your hips, shoulders, arms, and head. Now imagine that you're going for a walk somewhere over the Earth. Where do you go? What is your imaginary landscape? Who do you meet? To complete your imaginary journey, walk yourself back into the room you're actually in, and orient to your surroundings.

## Expressive Improvisations for Earth

Both the movement improvisations for Earth are explorations of body systems based on the Body/Mind Centering work of Bonnie Bainbridge Cohen (1993). By exploring our anatomy experientially, we gain access to a different way of knowing ourselves that can inform how we move, act, and feel. Body/Mind Centering (BMC) teaches that every physiological system has its own uniquely patterned quality of movement, and that it is possible to consciously access these bodily systems through movement (Eddy, 1998). For example, attending to the skeletal system tends to elicit movement that is precise, clear, and well-articulated. In contrast, movement initiated from the organs tends to have a voluminous, often ponderous quality. The organ system is under the direction of the autonomic, or involuntary, nervous system, and exploring this system through movement evokes information and feelings of a more unconscious nature. It is important to emphasize that in both examples, the actual movements are still being performed by the actions of muscles on bones, but the style and expression of the movement is different.

These movement improvisations are designed to expand our somatic awareness of two important body systems, as well as to explore contrasting movement qualities. Despite the physiological and experiential differences between bones and organs, both are significantly informed by the their relationship to Earth. The skeletal system depends upon alignment with gravity to function smoothly and effectively. (Think about the last time you twisted an ankle...) Although supported by hundreds of fascial attachments, our organs can still be thought of as the contents sloshing around in the container formed by our skeleton. Gravity pulls on them incessantly, despite the fact that we are so used to the pull that we hardly feel it. (Think of how your stomach felt on the way down a rollercoaster...) As you explore the movements that arise out of the following experiments, notice how they are similar as well as how they differ. What correlations might you draw to the differences and similarities between the organs and bones of your body?

## Dancing from the Bones

The adult human skeleton is a complex, movable framework of 206 bones, held together at the joints by ligaments. A common misconception is to think of the skeleton as a rigid, steel-like structure. Actually, bones are extremely flexible at birth and only grow harder as we age. The skeleton itself is designed to allow for a surprisingly wide range of movement. Also contrary to popular thought, bones are not made of solid inert material. They are dynamic, living tissues that need a supply of oxygen and nutrients just as do other parts of the body, and are actually composed of about 50% water.

The skeleton performs some very important functions in the body. First, it provides a supportive framework for our muscles, organs and tissues. In addition, bone marrow (the inside of the bone) produces all the blood cells required by our body, and bones store 99% of all the body s calcium. The skeleton also allows us to move -- it provides sites of attachment for muscles, and the long bones in our arms and legs act as levers that move according to the lengthening and shortening of the muscles attached to the bones.

- Bring your awareness to your bones. Starting with your fingers, begin to move in a way that articulates each joint. Let your bone dance travel up your hands to your arms and shoulders, and from there to your spine, pelvis, legs and feet. Dance as though you were just a skeleton. Once you have a clear somatic awareness of your bones in motion, notice how your bones serve as the structural foundation for your muscles, and as the container for your organs.

## Dancing from the Organs

Physiologically, organs are much different from bones. They are softer, more flexible, and often hollow. Where bones are primarily movers, organs are processors. Many of the body's organs are part of the digestive system, a continuous passage through the body that handles the input, processing, and output of food. This passage is made up of tubes of smooth muscle that move the food along from one organ, or processing station, to the next. Other organs, such as those involved in circulation and respiration, are explored in more depth in the sections on Air and Fire.

- Bring your awareness to your organs - your lungs, stomach, intestines, bladder, etc. Slowly begin to move in a way that allows your organs to slosh gently in the container provided by your pelvis and ribcage. Direct a soft wobbling or jiggling movement into your organs. Let your dance initiate from different organs - how does your movement change when it emerges from your lungs instead of your stomach, for example? How is your organ dance different from your bone dance?

## Cool Down for Earth

To make a gradual transition from active movement, walk slowly and quietly around the room until your breathing, heart-rate, and body temperature have returned to a comfortable state.

## Optional Exploration for Integrating Organs and Bones
(adapted from Bonnie Bainbridge Cohen's *Sensing, Feeling, and Action*)
- Lie comfortably on the floor. Without consciously interfering with it, become aware of your breathing.
- Allow the weight of your bones to fall into gravity. What do you notice as you consciously release your bones into the Earth? What happens to the quality of your breath?
- Allow the weight of your organs to fall into gravity. What do you notice as you consciously release your organs into the Earth? What happens to the quality of your breath?
- Allow yourself to change body position. How were your bones and organs involved in the movement?

## Interactive Improvisation for Earth

The interactive section of the Earth session is focused on an exploration of rhythm. Although we may ordinarily limit our conception of rhythm to the audible beat in music, rhythm is far more pervasive and fundamental than that. Rhythm is any movement or action with a uniform or patterned recurrence of elements. Movement creates rhythm through contrast. It is the repeated changes in movement quality throughout a sequence of movements that gives the sequence its rhythmic pattern. For example, the quality of contraction is different from the quality of release -- think of squeezing your hand into a fist and letting it go. When these two contrasting movements are repeated, a simple rhythm is created. These recurring patterns can be found everywhere in our world, especially in nature. The waves crashing on a beach follow a rhythm, the sun obeys a rhythm that forms night and day, and the leaves on the trees trace the long, slow rhythm of the seasons.

Rhythm is a phenomenon experienced very much on a body level -- it can be seen, heard, and felt, and all of these rhythmic perceptions are interrelated. The body itself is organized into rhythmic patterns. The beating of our hearts and the rising and falling of our breath are two of the most primary rhythms within the body. Longer rhythms include the digestive process and the menstrual cycle. The ways we talk and walk and work also naturally fall into rhythmic patterns. Walking is such a rhythmic activity that it takes enormous effort and concentration to walk without eventually developing a rhythm.

## Body Rhythms

The body is our primary rhythm instrument. Not only does it generate inherent rhythmic patterns - walking, breathing, pulsing - it possesses the capacity to create additional patterns through the use of sound and gesture. Here are some experiments to help you develop new ways to play your native rhythm instrument. As you experiment, it might be helpful to remember that rhythm does not need to be audible.

- Find a simple, easily repeatable gesture. Find another gesture that feels like a contrast to the first one. Alternate between the two gestures. Play with the intervals between gestures. Add a third gesture. Notice how the rhythm shifts.
- Share your rhythmic patterns with someone else. Repeat the patterns together. Is it easy or hard to be "in sync" with one another? Can you find a way to integrate both patterns? What rhythm have you created?
- To music with a simple but compelling beat, echo the rhythm by gently slapping different parts of your body to the beat. Start with your belly, then move to your chest, your back, your legs and arms. Notice how different parts of your body feel and sound. Make sure to reach every part of you.
- Find a way to share your rhythm with someone else - perhaps by moving together to the same beat, or creating a rhythm conversation (like the children's game of pattycake), or by gently tapping out a rhythm on part of their body.

Although this experiment is designed for individual, rather than interactive work, it is included here as an additional way to experiment somatically with rhythm.

- Using Ravel's *Bolero* as a blueprint, experiment with building on rhythm in the body. As the first rhythmic pattern is introduced in the music, follow it by echoing that rhythm with one part of your body - by contracting your pelvic floor or tapping your feet, for example. As the music adds instrumental themes, choose different body parts to represent them, and follow the musical theme with that part of the body. By the time the piece builds to a gradual climax, see if you can perform each of these movements simultaneously. Notice how it feels to have so many movements orchestrated together.

## Collective Movement Structures for Earth

### Rhythmic Synchrony

Rhythmic synchrony can have a remarkable effect on our somatic experience of others. This simple exercise illustrates the impact it can have.

- As a group, line up together at one end of the room. Starting at the same time, have everyone move across to the other side of the room at whatever reasonably quick pace feels right for them. Repeat the walk across the room, only this time have everyone move in perfect step with the others. (It helps if someone beats out an audible rhythm to follow.) Notice the difference in the two ways of walking. How did walking together affect your experience of the group, and your personal experience as part of it? Was one experience more "grounding" for you than the other?

### Eurhythmics

The following exercises are a fun way to play with rhythm in a group, and are based on a body-centered method of musical education called Eurhythmics. This method, developed by Swiss musician Emile Jacques-Dalcroze at the turn of the century, uses body movements to represent musical rhythms. The larger the group, the more fun these can be.

- Standing in a circle, pass a clap around the circle (each person in the circle claps once in turn, then the person next to them claps once, and so on...) Once the group has the hang of it, pass the clap both ways around the circle. Then pass the clap around the circle, but missing every other person.

## Expressive Arts Experiments for Earth

- Draw a picture of your skeletal system from your experience of dancing. Compare it to an anatomical rendering of the human skeleton if you'd like. Notice where they are similar as well as where they are different. Draw a picture of your organs in the same way.
- Write a story about meeting Mother Earth. What does she say to you, and what do you say to her?
- Compose a song using only rhythm. Teach it to someone.

# Water

*There's nothing very complicated about a water molecule: it's just one big oxygen atom with two little hydrogen atoms stuck to it like Mickey Mouse ears. Its behavior is governed by well-understood equations of atomic physics. But now put a few zillion of those molecules together in the same pot. Suddenly you've got a substance that shimmers and gurgles and sloshes. Those zillions of molecules have collectively acquired a property, liquidity, that none of them possesses alone... Cool those liquid water molecules down a bit...and they will suddenly quit tumbling over one another at random. Instead they will undergo a "phase transition", locking themselves into the orderly crystalline array known as ice. Or if you were to go the other direction and heat the liquid, those same tumbling water molecules will suddenly fly apart...*

- *from Complexity: The Emerging Science at the Edge of Order and Chaos (Waldrop, 1992, p. 82)*

As the preceding quote suggests, Water is perhaps the most mutable and complex of the Elements. Symbolically, it can evoke the cozy solace of a warm bath, or the unfathomable mystery of the deep. It is crushing tidal wave and placid pool, impervious ice and gentle rain. It contrast to the steady reliability of Earth, Water is wavering in its commitment to be any one thing for very long. Water runs hot and cold, as can our relationship with it. Water's capacity for multidimensional expression likens it to the human capacity for revealing our changing inner landscape through emotion. Like emotion, Water responds and permeates. It changes according to the situation, as well as reflecting it. The emotional component flows through the material that follows, and the many of the somatic experiments are designed specifically to include it.  In addition to Water's emotional affinities, the watery qualities of reflectiveness and flow are the focus of several movement explorations.

## Somatic Reflections for Water

### Inner Water

On a body level, our relationship with Water occurs on a primary cellular level.   Our bodies are composed more of water than anything else.   Every cell is filled with and bathed in fluid. Through osmosis, the movement of fluids through the cell membrane, water brings nourishment and removes waste.   The fluid in our bodies lubricates our muscles and joints - without water, our bodies could not move.

•   Take a moment and allow your body to move in a way that connects you to the fluidity within.

### Waves and Tides

The effect of lunar rhythms on the earth's magnetic field creates the ebb and flow we know as the tide.  All the water on the planet, from the deepest oceans to the water inside each tiny cell in our body, moves in tides.

•   Take a moment and imagine the ebb and flow within yourself, down to each cell.   Repeat the Fundamentals   Heel Rock described in the Activating Explorations in the Earth section, this time allowing yourself to notice the wavelike rippling that runs from head to foot.

### Going with the Flow

Water is the universal solvent - dissolving what is tight or hard and rendering a liquid solution.   Water is ubiquitous, seeping through and into everything everywhere.  Water allows us to go with the flow.

•   Find a place in your body - or an issue in your life - that feels inflexible or impenetrable.   Without force or effort, imagine gently bathing this part of you in Water. What happens? Try moving the bathed part.

*Nothing in the world is as soft and yielding as water.*
*Yet for dissolving the hard and inflexible, nothing can*
*surpass it.*

*- Tao Te Ching (as quoted in Kastner, 1996, p.336)*


## Sensory Dimensions of Water

On a sensory level, the element of Water may evoke a range of sensations and qualities.

- When you imagine Water, what sounds come to your mind's ear? Sometimes I hear the clear pinging sound of raindrops or the laughing of a mountain stream. The soft rolling hush of ocean waves also speaks to me of Water.
- What colors feel like Water to you? Is it the deep turquoise blue of a glacial lake, the pale shimmery green of a quiet pond, the silvery white of winter snow? Imagine one and immerse yourself in it.
- How does Water smell? The salty tang of the sea or the fresh green smell of a spring rain might be Watery smells for you. Imagine your favorite and take a deep breath.
- If I were going to get a taste of Water, I'd be biting into something, well, wet and juicy. But also clean and tangy and fresh. Iced peppermint tea does it for me. What tastes are evocative of Water for you?

*Song*
*The great sea*
*Has set me adrift,*
*It moves me as the weed in a great river,*
*Earth and the great weather*
*Move me,*
*Have carried me away*
*And move my inward parts with joy.*

*- Uvavnuk (Ireland, The Poet's Craft, p.54)*

## Elemental Mantra

The Sanskrit letter for the Element of Water is Va. You may use it as part of a mantra-centered meditation by repeating it silently with each breath for a period of 15 or 20 minutes while resting quietly.


# Activating Explorations for Water

The active circulation of the body's intrinsic fluid systems is central to the somatic experience of feeling "warmed-up". Body temperature gradually increases as arterial and venous blood flow is accelerated. Slow movements in the full range of motion stimulates the production of synovial fluid, lubricating the joints and preparing them for movement. Movement through the edge of the kinesphere creates peripheral tension in the tissue, stimulating the circulation of lymph from deep and superficial tissue layers to central drainage areas located in the torso. Activated lymphatic fluids prepare the body to resist the effects of toxins that may be released by aerobic activity. Movement of the muscles in the pelvic floor assists the circulation of the cerebrospinal fluid, which nourishes and protects the nervous system. As you engage in the explorations for activation that follow, see if you can notice and consciously include the type of movements suggested above.


## Bodypainting

(adapted from Andrea Olsen's *Bodystories*)
This activation experiment allows us to lubricate joints and awaken the proprioceptive sense. Imagine that you are lying in a pool of liquid color that covers the surface of the floor around you. This pool of color can be any shade you like, but you might want to choose a color that suggests Water to you - maybe blues, greens, or silvery-grays. Give yourself a moment to envision a shade you really love. Begin very slowly to paint the entire surface of your skin by moving the surface of your body in contact with the floor. Roll around so all the surfaces of each part of your body is covered with the color. Be sure to cover every part of you - your back, your belly, your head, the soles of your feet. You can use a part of

113

your body that is already covered in color to access hard-to-reach areas - between your toes, behind your ears, under your chin. When you are completely covered, take a moment to stretch or wriggle. Take a breath. Imagine yourself as a living watercolor sculpture.

## Synovial Fluid Activation

This warm-up experiment uses large, easy movements to stimulate the production of synovial fluid in your joints. Keeping your feet connected to the ground, begin to move your body and arms as if you were swimming in a deep pool of water. Practice your front crawl and your dog paddle. Try to capture the smooth, weightless sensation of moving in water. Imagine a quality of spaciousness in each of your joints. Reach fully into every stroke. Finish your experiment by slowly pouring your body into the ground - rolling forward from your spine and bending your knees until you reach the floor. Now let yourself spread out like a puddle, and soak into the earth.

## Water Stretch

This hamstring stretch also serves as a stretch for the Kidney/Bladder meridian used in Chinese medicine, which is governed by the Element of Water.

* Stand with feet parallel, shoulder-width apart, with one foot about eight to ten inches in front of the other. Keeping the front leg straight, slowly lower your body by bending the back leg, as if you were going to sit down on a chair. Your body weight is on the back supporting leg. You can lean forward slightly and rest your hands on your supporting leg for balance. Stop when you feel a slight pulling stretch along the back of the thigh of your extended front leg. Hold the stretch for about 30 seconds, or as long as you feel comfortable. You should not feel any pull or pressure in any of your joints. Breathe. Repeat on the other side.

114

# Expressive Improvisations for Water

*Water - the ace of Elements. Water dives from clouds without parachute, wings, or safety net. Water runs over the steepest precipice and blinks not a lash. Water is buried and rises again; water walks on fire and fire gets the blisters. Stylishly composed in any situation - solid, gas, or liquid - speaking in penetrating dialects understood by all things - animal, vegetable or mineral - water travels intrepidly through four dimensions, sustaining (Kick a lettuce in the field and it will yell "Water!"), destroying (The Dutch boy's finger remembered the view from Ararat) creating (It has even been said that human beings were invented by water as a device for transporting itself from one place to another, but that's another story). Always in motion, ever-flowing (whether at steam rate or glacier speed), rhythmic, dynamic, ubiquitous, changing and working its changes, a mathematics turned wrong side out, a philosophy in reverse, the ongoing odyssey of water is virtually irresistable.*

*- Tom Robbins, Even Cowgirls Get the Blues*

One of the most significant movement attributes of Water is its remarkable quality of flow. In this context, our exploration of flow will be based on the work of movement analyst Rudolf Laban. According to Laban, the term *flow*[18] is used to denote a property of movement that pertains to the sequence of fluency and restraint in the state of muscles in movement and at rest (Bartenieff, 1980). It traces the increase and decrease of muscle tension during movement. The attributes of flow depend on several factors, including frequency, intensity, and rate of increase or decrease. It is primarily distinguished, however, by qualities of being free or bound. Bound flow is an inhibited quality of movement in which the movement can be easily stopped. Free flow is an uninhibited quality that cannot be easily stopped at will.

---

[18] Note that Laban's use of the term *flow* differs from that of Czicsentmihalyi as discussed in the chapter on Inner Alchemy.

On a physiological level, flow of tension refers to the relationship between the agonist and antagonist muscles involved in the movement (Kestenberg, 1971). If the antagonist is relaxed, the movement will tend to have a free flow. If the antagonist is tense, or strongly contracted in relation to the agonist, the movement flow will be more bound. Extremely free flow leads to the overshooting of movement seen in young children - falling, spilling, knocking things over. Extremely bound flow leads to rigid immobilization.

Some general connections may also be drawn between qualities of flow and the emotional mood those movements invoke (Kestenberg, 1971). Free flow often evokes carefree feelings, while bound flow may elicit cautious feelings. An even intensity of free flow might suggest serene, steady confidence, where an even intensity of bound flow could hint at concern or apprehension. Elation, depression, surprise, fright, pleasant expectation, and uneasy foreboding are also expressible in the body through alternations in movement flow.

- Find a piece of music that feels to you as though it flows. (Perhaps a waltz...) Allow yourself to move in waves, in a way that ebbs and flows. Let motion ripple along your arms, legs, and spine. Pour yourself from one movement to the next. Notice your emotional response to the music and the movement.
- Write a brief description of a previous emotional experience. Then relate that same experience through movement. Notice the qualities of flow in your movement. Notice if your movement expressed the experience differently than your words.

## Cool Down for Water
To make a gradual transition from active movement, move languidly through the room as though you are treading water. Slow your movements until your breathing, heart-rate, and body temperature have returned to a comfortable state.

# Interactive Improvisation for Water

## Kinesthetic Reflections

A tranquil pool of Water was probably our ancestor's first source of personal reflection. This interactive movement structure is designed to elicit and explore the mirroring capacity of Water.

- Stand facing a partner, several feet apart. Bring your arms in front of you so that your palms are facing and almost touching your partner's. Without verbally guiding the process, begin to move your hands so that your movements echo or mirror each other. Continue with the movement for several minutes. You may want to use flowing music as a quiet background.

- What happened to your somatic awareness as you focused on the interplay of movement between you and your partner? How was your breathing during the exercise? What emotions were you aware of? Were there moments where the movement really seemed to "flow"? What supported those moments? What about times when the movement got stuck or stiff? How might this experience relate to experiences of interpersonal fluidity and/or constriction in your life?

- Notice how you felt when you were "leading" the movement, and how it felt to have your actions reflected by your partner. What happened when their reflections were experienced by you as distorted? How did you feel when you were doing most of the reflecting? Are your responses familiar to you from other life situations?

An interesting variation on this exercise is possible without an actual partner physically present. Instead, visualize a partner in your mind's eye - you might choose a parent or spouse, or you could create an imaginary one. After moving, explore your experience using questions similar to those above.

# Collective Movement Structure for Water

### Rhythmic Raindance

This movement experiment is designed to recreate the sound of a rainstorm, and to explore Water's wilder side. It works best in larger groups where the sound really has time to build. The raindrop sound is created by tapping and slapping the thighs.

- Sit or stand in a circle facing each other. Choose someone to lead the movement. The leader begins by making a soft, slow raindrop sound on their thighs, "Plop, plop...". They continue to make the same sound as each person in turn adds their raindrops to the sound storm. When the first raindrop pattern has traveled all the way around the circle, the leader changes the sound to a faster, louder pattern. This, in turn, travels around the circle. Finally, the leader initiates a furious raindrop. After the rainstorm reaches its peak, the leader slows the storm down by initiating a slower, quieter tapping pattern. The last circle consists of the same soft slow plopping that began the storm.

Note: The key to this exercise is for everyone to continue to make the sound that was passed to them until the next sound is passed their way. Playing with "arrhythmic" raindrops adds to the realism of this exercise. You can also add vocal "thunder" to the rainstorm.

## Expressive Arts Experiments for Water

- Create a watercolor drawing or finger painting by tracing along a large sheet of paper using free flow. Do the same using bound flow.
- Write a poem about how you are like the rain, the ocean, the snow, a lake, or a river. Choose a part of your body to embody the poem. Then have that part recite the poem without words.
- Play with flow using your voice. Begin by creating a single stream of sound, then create ripples in the stream by changing the shape of your mouth and tongue.

# Air

On a somatic level, our primary relationship with Air occurs through breathing. At the deepest somatic layer, breathing is cellular. This is the basic level upon which all our life processes depend. It is in the cells that our breath is transformed. At the outermost layer is respiration through our lungs. Breathing is an exchange - bringing the external environment into the internal environment, letting go of the inside to the outside (Olsen, 1991). Through our breathing relationship with Air, we dialogue with the outer world.

The Element of Air also influences another important way we interact with our environment - through our use of space. Relating to our spatial environments requires more than orientation to gravity and the basic skills of locomotion. It requires the development of body shaping and the ability to respond to the spatial requirements of each situation. As we expand our spatial dexterity, we also become more perceptive. The invisible nuances of the Element of Air, such as atmosphere and ambiance, become more easily discernible. As we learn to navigate the personal use of shared space, the related issues of interpersonal boundaries and proxemics[19] emerge.

When our somatic relationship with Air is strong and clear, we allow ourselves to take up space, and to interact freely with it and in it. We breathe easily in response to our changing environments, whether physical, social, or psychological. The feelings of freedom and inspiration that Air evokes become ours to access and enjoy. Where Earth gives us ground to stand on, Air gives us wings to fly.

---

[19] Proxemics involves the study of communication by and through the use of space.

# Somatic Reflections for Air

The respiratory system is in charge of obtaining a sufficient supply of oxygen for the body s metabolic needs, and disposing of the waste products of metabolism. Oxygen is available in the air around us (about 20% of the air is composed of oxygen), and is taken into the body through the nose and mouth. The nose is lined with tiny hairs which help to filter the incoming air, and with mucous to help increase the air s moisture content. These air passages also warm or cool the outside air to bring its temperature closer to the body s internal temperature. On its way to the lungs, air passes over the vocal cords in the larynx, which are capable of producing sound by shaping and vibrating the column of air as it passes. The incoming air is pulled into the lungs by the internal vacuum created by the dropping of the large, strong diaphragm muscle that sits just underneath the lungs. It is the movement of the diaphragm and the assisting bellows-like movements of the ribcage that shapes the size and duration of each breath. The two experiments below focus on expanding our somatic awareness of breathing.

## Dimensional Breath

- Lie down comfortably on your back. Allow yourself to breathe the way you would if you were falling asleep. Without changing anything, notice how you are breathing. Slowly and gradually allow your breath to expand into your upper chest. Slowly and gradually expand your breath side to side. Now expand your breath down into the floor. Finally, expand your breath into your belly. When you exhale, imagine that you are blowing a tiny feather high up into the sky. Keep breathing out until the feather disappears from sight, and allow your next inhale to come by itself. Now go back to breathing as if you were falling asleep.

## Exploring the Respiratory System

(adapted from Andrea Olsen's *Bodystories*)
To experience your own respiratory system at work, try these simple body awareness exercises. They will work best if you can do them in a relaxed, unhurried manner.

- Lie on your back, with your hands on your chest, over your lungs. Breathe in through your nose, and feel the air in your nose as it rushes in. Breathe out, gently forcing the air out through your nose in short little puffs. Feel how your nose and nasal passages are involved in each breath.
- Breathe in through your nose, allowing your larynx to vibrate on the inhalation, so that it makes a humming sound. Breathe out, also making a humming sound. Notice the difference in how the breaths sound and feel. Make some more humming sounds, allowing them to resonate from deeper in your chest each time. Feel the volume of your chest cavity through the vibrations of your soundings.
- Breathe in and out, and feel your chest rise and fall with each breath. Notice that your chest expands in all directions, in width as well as height. Feel your ribs moving. Trace your ribcage with your hands.
- Place your hands on your diaphragm, and feel it move as you breathe. Turn over onto your stomach, and feel your diaphragm move against the floor.
- Roll over onto your side, in a semi-fetal position. As you breathe, feel your ribs and spine moving. Put your hands on different places on your back, and feel them move as your breathe. Breathe in, and imagine filling the concave space between your shoulder blades with breath. Notice again that your ribcage has depth.
- Roll back onto your back. Breathe in deeply, as if you were breathing down into your abdomen. Place your hands on your belly as you breathe to help you feel it move.
- Bring your awareness to all of the parts of your body you ve felt during these exercises. Notice how much of your body moves when you breathe.
- Slowly stretch and yawn before getting up.


## Body Boundaries

This next somatic reflection experiment relates to the dimension of the Element of Air that has to do with space and boundaries. On a somatic level, we experience boundaries most directly through our skin. The skin forms the external barrier between our bodies and

121

the environment. It is a highly sensitive and responsive membrane that is actually the largest organ in the body. The skin keeps the water inside the body from evaporating and regulates body temperature. It sweats and blushes to help the body rid itself of excess heat; to conserve body heat, it closes down its blood supply. The skin also provides sites for many of the body s sensory receptors, including the ones for heat, pain, and touch. This experiment offers one way to explore your body boundaries through touch.

- Using your hands or a soft brush, gently stroke the whole surface of your skin. As you stimulate the touch receptors in your skin, what happens to your experience of separateness and connection to the external environment? How do you experience your boundaries?

## Sensory Dimensions of Air

On a sensory level, the element of Air may evoke a range of sensations and qualities.

- When you imagine Air, what sounds come to your mind's ear? Do you hear the wild howling of a hurricane, or the faint whisper of a breeze? Perhaps you hear wind chimes, or harps, or the sound of angelic voices...
- What colors feel like Air to you? Is it the deep limitless blue of the summer sky? The downy pinks and mauves of the clouds tinted by the setting sun? The leaden gray of a sky threatening rain? Wrap yourself in an Air color.
- How does Air smell? When I think of Air, I imagine the scent of clean sheets fresh off the line, or the soft, dark smell of a summer night. Imagine your favorite and take a deep lungful.
- If I were going to get a taste of Air, it would be light and sweet. Whipped cream with a hint of vanilla, or angelfood cake. Maybe both. What tastes are evocative of Air for you?

*Figure 3*

## Elemental Mantra

The Sanskrit letter for the Element of Air is Ya. You may use it as part of a mantra-centered meditation by repeating it silently with each breath for a period of 15 or 20 minutes while resting quietly.

## Activation Experiment for Air

Each movement of our body carves shapes in space, and awareness of the range of our shaping possibilities is one of the keys to understanding our bodily use of space. In much the same way that a graphic artist learns to attend to both the black and white space on the page in understanding the overall design of their work, we can learn to attend to movement as related to our bodies and to space. Space is the white page upon which we imprint the fleeting dimensional impressions of our bodies.

The first task in relating to space is evaluating the spatial qualities of our immediate personal environment. By taking the full range of motion of all of the parts of the body and tracing them in space, we can begin to outline the body's spatial zones. For example, circling your arm from your shoulder as far around your body as you can - to the front, across, up, back and to the side - delineates its spatial zone. Knowing the spatial zones of each of the major body parts enriches the conscious awareness of the movement shaping possibilites of that part. By imagining the largest scope of length, width and depth that the body could reach while standing upright, we can create a sense of the three-dimensional space around the body. This reach space around the body is called the *kinesphere*. This kinesphere has three dimensions - length, width, and depth. The space beyond the kinesphere also possesses the same qualities of dimension, and we use our understanding of it every time we engage in locomotion, ie. when we move our our kinespheres through space.

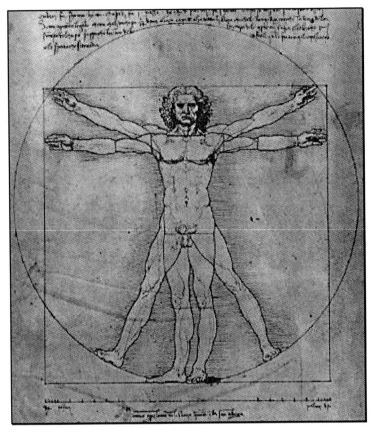

*Figure 4*

### Exploring the Kinesphere

- Trace the spatial zones of your arms, legs, and head. Notice how you can extend the spatial zones of your limbs by bending your upper body.
- Trace the edges of your kinesphere with your hands and feet.

- When you have finished mapping the outlines of your kinesphere, take a few steps, still feeling the sense of the three-dimensional space around your body.
- Holding onto a length of ribbon, trace your kinesphere again. Notice how the ribbon extends your personal space. Let the ribbon dance around the whole interior of this extended kinesphere. How do you shape your body in order to reach every part of your kinesphere with the ribbon?
- Try visualizing your personal space as a cube instead of a sphere. How does this change the way you shape your body? How does it affect your somatic experience?[20]
- Now move through the room, still using your body and the ribbon to carve different shapes in space. How does moving in this way affect your perception of the spatial relationship between your body and the environment? Is this similar or different to your experience of body boundaries through touch explored in the Somatic Reflections experiment?

The use of space is one of the key factors in analyzing movement, and the Laban system of Movement Analysis (LMA) has developed movement "scales" to delineate that space. Like practicing musical scales, these Space Harmony Scales take the body through all the various locations and dimensions of the kinesphere. Performing these scales involves a range of evocative reaching, sweeping, bowing, and gathering motions, and can be beautiful to watch as well as to do. One of these scales, called the A-Scale, elicited Elemental images for a Laban Movement Analyst, and a poem based on her experience is included here:

---

[20] As well as generating a range of somatic experience, the different shapes our bodies create appear to elicit characteristic emotional reactions as well. For example, psychologist Joel Aronoff and his colleagues at Michigan State University have discovered that open, rounded postures were typically assigned a sympathetic character, where sharp, angular gestures conveyed a sense of threat or danger (Pleasing Shapes, *Allure*, 1993). Aronoff speculates that these consistent emotional responses to shapes may have evolved from a biological mechanism in the brain designed to read expression in order to respond quickly and appropriately to important interpersonal signals.

*An Inner Vision of the A-Scale*
*by Vivian Ytterhus*

*Gather the radiance of the Sky*
*Plunge it into the Earth's Fire*
*And give it to the Earth Deva...*

*Glean Earth's inner power*
*Whisk it through higher dimensions*
*And spread it on the Wind...*

*Take Earth's Water*
*Raise it to the Sky*
*And let it cascade back to Earth...*

*Bring the Fire of the Pleiades*
*With reverence to the Earth Mother*
*Retreat to the Earth plane...*

*To reach again for Sky radiance.*

*(Association of Laban Movement Analysts (ALMA)*
*News, Fall 1989)*

## Expressive Improvisation for Air

The following movement improvisations are designed to explore the relationship between breath and space. You may also discover some connections between motion and emotion as you move.

### Dancing on Air

- Choose a piece of music that evokes Airy qualities for you[21], and find a large chiffon scarf to dance with. Begin by noticing the movement of your own breath. As you breathe, allow the movement of your breath to expand. Use your scarf to echo

---

[21] In terms of musical selection for this exercise, I often use *Caribbean Blue* by Enya or *Lark Ascending* by Ralph Vaughn Williams.

the movement of your breath. Allow your scarf to begin its own dance, to expand into space, and to carve the space into shapes. Try to keep the movements of your scarf connected in some way to your breath. Move from the lightness and Airiness in your being. What sensations and emotions emerge as you dance?

## Cloud Dancing

• Imagine that you are floating in masses of fluffy white clouds high in the sky. Navigate through the clouds using your breath to stay aloft and your movements to direct your body in space. As you move, the clouds begin to darken and swirl together. A rainstorm is building. Let your movements reflect this change in your environment. Let the stormclouds buffet you around until eventually you are rained out of the sky. Allow your body to fall to earth as if it were a drop of rain.

# Interactive Improvisation for Air

• If you wish to expand the preceding exercise to the interpersonal dimension, use your scarf and your breath to explore the space in the room and between people. Allow your scarf to dance with the scarves of others. Notice the shapes the scarves carve in space. Notice how you interact with other people using your scarf. How is this different from how you might dance with them without a scarf?

## Cool Down for Air

After dancing on Air, use your breath to gradually slow your movements down until your rate of breathing has returned to normal. Be sure to keep your feet moving as you cool down. Finish your cool down with some stretches, paying special attention to your upper body. Imagine the muscles you would use if you had wings attached to your shoulder blades, and give your flying muscles an extra good stretch.

## Interpersonal Dimensions of Space

Our relationship with the spatial environment deepens when we include the human dimension. An empty subway car is a very different space when you add the presence of even a few people, and the difference is as much psychological as it is physical. In addition to affecting our perceptions of the space, human presence also brings into play a set of behavioral codes involving the interpersonal use of space. How we manage the space between people is a powerful form of nonverbal communication, and the nature of this communication colors our perception of our place in the larger spatial environment.

The study of the communication by and through the use of space is called proxemics. Based on early research on animal's defense of territory that led to parallel investigations of human territoriality, proxemics explores the many dimensions and permutations of spatial communication. For example, research has suggested cultural variations in the distance people use for formal and informal conversational interactions, and that deviations from the cultural norm communicate something beyond the usual (Hall, 1963). Other researchers (Patterson, 1968) have noted that individuals may employ compensatory measures to moderate an uncomfortable or unwanted amount of interpersonal distance. Leaning towards or away from the other person, breaking eye contact, or shifting the body sideways are all forms of compensation. Immediacy cues, such as distance, body orientation, and eye gaze, were also found by Mehrabian (1971) to convey the degree of intimacy and affection involved in a relationship.

Group dynamics may also be reflected proxemically - subsets may cluster together, deviant group members may be rejected by physical distancing, and those in leadership roles may position themselves centrally in order to communicate their status to the rest of the group. Sommer (1969) found that people also use the spatial features in the environment to communicate information about their relationship to others. Someone who situates themselves at the very end of a table, for example, or arranges their books, coats, and purses as territorial markers conveys strategic information about that person. What do you notice about the way you characteristically use space to communicate to others?

## Defining Interpersonal Boundaries

    The following experiment uses movement as a way to explore our interpersonal use of space, and our experience of creating boundaries within the space we share with others. As you work, keep in mind that everyone has different needs for space, based on individual preference, gender roles, cultural background, and current circumstance. There is no ideal standard to which one should aspire.

- Stand facing your partner, about 10 feet apart. Have your partner begin by slowly moving toward you. Attend to your own inner somatic experience, and notice when you become aware of signals indicating that your own personal boundaries have been reached. At that point, tell your partner to stop advancing. When your partner stops, you may wish to ask them to retreat a half-step to ensure they are not inside your personal boundary. When you are ready, switch roles with your partner.
- Share with your partner your experience of having them approach you to the limits of your own personal space. What were the somatic indicators that a boundary had been reached? Was the boundary in the same place for both people, i.e. could your partner have continued to approach you without becoming uncomfortable? How was your relationship with space and boundaries related to breath?
- On your own, examine the implications of your personal experience of boundaries. To what extent might they be affected by personal traits or attitudes, the expectations of your gender and culture, or the relationship you have with your working partner?

# Collective Movement Structures for Air

    The first collective movement structure for Air explores how we can experience the use of space as a cooperative group venture. It extends the awareness of interpersonal boundaries developed in the preceding experiment to the unique conditions of a group context.

- Everyone begins by walking all at once around the room, using all the space. Go to every place in the room that you can.
- Start moving increasingly faster.
- As you move with more speed, you will find yourself encountering others with more frequency. When you approach someone, or are approached by them, move so that you give them as much space as you possibly can.
- Notice how your awareness of space changes with speed, and with the intention of giving up, rather than taking, space.

The second collective movement structure for Air is based on a group exploration of balancing private space with shared space.

- The group begins by standing together in a circle. Each member of the group begins to move in whatever way feels right for them in the moment. Allow a simple, repeatable movement to emerge for each person. Without deliberate direction, allow these individual movements to evolve into a single collective group movement. Have everyone in the circle repeat this movement together.
- One the group movement is established, individual members of the group may spontaneously leave the circle in order to return to their own individual movement, or to develop new movements. While individuals are free to come and go from the circle as they wish, three people must remain in the circle at any given time to maintain the group movement signature. The experiment can be brought to a close when everyone who wishes has had an opportunity move both inside and outside the circle.
- How did you take care of your needs for personal space in this context? Were your spatial preferences affected by whether you were inside or outside the circle? How?
- Compare your findings to your real-life experiences of being in groups.

The final interpersonal improvisation for Air offers yet another context for examining the interpersonal use of space, and combines it with an exploration of the Airy qualities of space, lightness, and breath.

## Balloon Dance

- Have the group form a loose circle. Begin by tossing a single balloon into the air. As the balloon falls, any group member who wishes can tap the balloon so that it stays in the air. The group task is to keep the balloon continuously aloft.
- Although the group task is to keep the balloon in the air, it is not the object of the experiment. As you participate in the group task, notice what happens to your breathing. Notice what happens to your awareness of body shaping, use of space, and group proxemics. How might you extrapolate this awareness to other contexts in which the focus of attention is on a single group activity?

# Expressive Arts Experiments for Air

- Write a poem or story about being able to fly.
- Compose an Air song/poem using only your breath and the shapings of your mouth and lips (not your vocal cords).
- Create a mobile, windchime, windsock, or kite. Infuse your creation with symbols and qualities of the Element of Air.

# Fire

*Fire is fundamental to the alchemical/psychological process of distillation. In alchemy, its purpose was to extract the volatile substance, or spirit, from the body and then return the refined essence back to the body. The fire used in such a process originates from the center, carrying everything upwards as it burns. When the purified distillate cools, it falls back into the center, clarifying and refining it.*

*- Carl Jung (1967, p.150)*

Fire can be the most challenging Element to consciously embody. Although all the Elements possess a "shadow" side, they are not usually approached with wariness, or perceived as potentially volatile. Fire is often the exception. In most circumstances, its capacity to burn and destroy is as obvious as its capacity to warm and arouse. Like human passion, it can be a challenge to ensure that Fire does not rage out of control. For this reason, the somatic exploration of the Element of Fire can be especially valuable. By exploring the limits and effects of our energy, our passion, and our power, we develop skills. By embodying qualities we may mistrust, we make them our own. We come to have faith in our ability to use Fire's gifts wisely.

Many of the somatic explorations in this chapter center on Fire's capacity to generate energy. On a fundamental somatic level, this is expressed through our metabolism. We are literally burning in every cell in every moment. When cells combust oxygen in the process of creating energy, many of the body systems explored through other Elements are involved. Chemically, the metabolic process looks like this: Food + Oxygen = Energy + Water + Carbon Dioxide. On an

Elemental level, metabolism could be represented this way: Earth + Air = Fire + Water + (?). The activating explorations for Fire use simple aerobic exercises to explore our somatic capacity to create Fire.

Experiencing how Fire can be embodied also leads to explorations of the heart, both as the seat of our passions and as the pump that carries oxygenated blood to the cells. The Somatic Reflections for Fire offer some ways to get in touch with the basic life rhythm of our pulse, and one of the Collective Movement Structures uses the metaphoric heart center of the body to create a circle of interpersonal connection and warmth.

In addition to Fire's connection with passionate intensity and heart energy, it can also represent a process of purification. In a somatic context, the body uses fever to purify itself when infected by bacteria. Fire is also associated with enlightenment and illumination - the Chinese trigram for Fire - *Li* - also means clarity, brightness, and intelligence. Fire allows us to brighten dark corners, and to see clearly where once there were only shadows.

## Somatic Reflections for Fire

### Pulsing Warmth

On a somatic level, our experience of the element of Fire is related to the creation and flow of energy and heat in our body. From a Western anatomical perspective, this involves the circulatory system that carries the nourishment our cells transform into heat and energy through metabolism. The flow of this energy is rhythmic, and can be felt as our pulse.

- Take a moment and find your own pulse[22] - either carotid, radial, or directly on the left lower ribcage. Be sure to press

---

[22] Our pulse is created by the rhythmic contraction of our heart. On a purely anatomical level, the heart is a hollow, muscular organ with four chambers that acts as a double pump. It is the working center of the circulatory system, the rest of which is made up of blood vessels, such as arteries, veins, and capillaries. At certain places in the body, major arteries are close enough to the surface to allow us to feel the

very gently on the carotid artery, and on one side only. This artery supplies blood to the brain, so it s important not to interrupt its flow. With your hands, find a place on your body where you feel most connected to a sense of your own body heat or warmth.

- If you'd like to explore your pulse from a quantitative perspective, you can find your own heart-rate in several ways. The most direct method is to place your hand over your heart, and count the beats. Because heart-rates are expressed in number of beats per minute, count the number of beats you feel in 10 seconds, and then multiply that number by 6. This method will give you a reasonably accurate count without having to keep track for the whole 60 seconds. The average resting heart-rate is about 70 beats per minute, although normal rates can vary. In general, the stronger (and therefore more efficient) the heart muscle, the lower the resting heart-rate.


## Energy Flow

From an Eastern perspective, the energy that flows through our body is known as *chi* (in Chinese), *ki* (in Japanese), or *kundalini* (in Hindu). This universal energy travels through our body along certain pathways, and the free unobstructed flow of this energy is considered essential for overall health and vitality. Certain areas of the body are related to different energy pathways, and the area connected to the flow of "heart" energy is located in the center of the chest at the level of the nipples.

- Take a moment and cover your heart *reflex area* or heart *chakra*[23] with both hands. As you connect with the warmth,

---

blood pumping through them. There are several of these pulse points on the body; one of them is at the side of the neck (called the carotid pulse, after the carotid artery that runs in front of the sternocleidomastoid muscle), and another at the wrist (called the radial pulse).

[23] The heart reflex area and the heart chakra are approximately the same place in the body - in the center of the chest at the level of the nipples. *Reflex area* is a term used in shiatsu, and is originally Japanese. The term *chakra* is Indian in origin, and derives from Kundalini yoga.

imagine this radiant heart energy flowing through your whole body, filling it with energy and warmth.

## Sensory Dimensions of Fire

On a sensory level, the element of fire evokes a range of sensations and qualities.

- When you imagine Fire, what sounds come to your mind's ear? Do you hear the roaring of a forest fire, or the soft crackling of the hearth?
- What colors feel like Fire to you? Is it the intense crimson of the setting sun? The palest yellows of a single flame? Wrap yourself in a Fire color.
- How does Fire smell? When I think of Fire, I inhale the soft smokiness of burning leaves, or the heavy sweetness of sandalwood incense. Imagine your favorite Fire smell and take a deep breath.
- If I were going to get a taste of Fire, it would be hot and spicy. For me, fiery tastes are the gingery and peppery flavors of Indian or Caribbean cuisine. What tastes are evocative of Fire for you?

## Elemental Mantra

The Sanskrit letter for the Element of Fire is Ra. You may use it as part of a mantra-centered meditation by repeating it silently with each breath for a period of 15 or 20 minutes while resting quietly.

# Activating Explorations for Fire

## Dancing from the Muscles

The activation exploration for Fire is designed to expand somatic awareness of the muscular system, and to warm-up the body cardiovascularly. In aerobic exercise programs (*aerobic* meaning literally *in the presence of oxygen*), the cardiovascular system is allowed to increase its activity gradually. A gradual increase in activity allows the system time to prepare for the increased demand for oxygen from the muscles as activity continues. Most cardiovascular warm-ups involve some form of easy locomotion, such as walking. This warm-up experientially explores some of the major muscle groups of the body.

- Walk slowly around the room at a leisurely pace. Breathe fully and easily.
- After a couple of minutes of walking, you should begin to feel warmer. At this point, begin to explore different muscles in your body by exaggerating their movement as you walk.
- As you walk, pick your feet up higher, as though you were walking through mud or tall wet grass. Where in your body do you feel this movement? What muscles seem to be involved? After you've had a chance to explore a bit, return your walk to normal.
- Next walk forward, but kick your feet backward behind you with each step. Now what muscles seem to be involved?
- As you continue, swing your arms more, as though you were skiing cross-country. Where in your body do you feel this movement? What muscles seem to be involved? After you've had a chance to explore a bit, return your walk to normal.
- Try different ways of walking that explore different muscles in your body. When you are finished exploring, you should be warmed-up sufficiently to go on to the movement improvisation that follows.

## Expressive Improvisation for Fire

The movement qualities of Fire fluctuate from raging blaze to a tranquil flicker.

Fire glows, smolders, dances, and sparks. In the body, the movements of Fire might be reflected as a flick of the hand, with all the lightness, quickness, and directness that entails. Fire might also be expressed as the slow, expansive undulations of a burning ember. The Fire improvisation that follows allows you to play with Fire in all its aspects, while at the same time generating body heat.

### Fire Dance

- Imagine you are going to light a Fire within you. This Fire begins slowly as a tiny spark somewhere inside your body. Once you have discovered where the Fire has been lit, use the

136

movements of your body to slowly fan the flame so that it flickers and glows. When you're ready, allow the Fire to catch and spread to other parts of your body. Use your breath to give the Fire the Air that it needs to expand. Once enough of your body has caught on Fire, its intensity will naturally build. Let the Fire blaze as brightly as you wish.

- As you naturally begin to run out of breath, your Fire will dwindle. Allow your inner Fire to gradually evolve from raging inferno to glowing embers. Use your movements to gather the embers into a safe place in your body, where they can be an enduring source of warmth and inner radiance.

## Interactive Improvisation for Fire

In his book, *Care of the Soul*, Thomas Moore talks about organic eroticism, and the importance of enjoying the sensual experience of moving. In Western culture, the expression of this enjoyment is often limited to young children, or is seen only in formalized expressions, such as in the art of dance performance. One of the most compelling emotional expressions of Fire can be seen in the focused intensity of flamenco dancers. Their eyes smolder and blaze, directing energy outwards to the object of their attention - the audience or their partner. Emotional heat radiates from them as if every cell in their body were on fire. Despite (or perhaps because of) the cultural constraints around expressing this energy through movement, Fire dancing with someone can be a thoroughly liberating and empowering experience.

- Using the same process as the individual Fire Dance above, light a somatic Fire in the presence of a partner. When you feel ready, send some of your Fire energy toward your partner. Play with the exchange of movement and energy between you as you dance. Let your movement flames begin to entwine and then flicker away again.
- How does your inner Fire change in response to your partner's Fire? How does the quality of your partner's Fiery energy compare with yours?

# Collective Movement Structures for Fire

### Heart Fire

The hearth or campfire has been a gathering place for tribes and families throughout the centuries, and its capacity to evoke feelings of connection and collective energy is remarkable. This movement structure uses the body's heart center as the conduit for the relational connectivity of touch, set within with the circular form of the home fire. This exercise needs a fairly large group to work well, and requires group members to be agreeable to having someone touch them on the back.

* The group forms a tight circle by sitting cross-legged on the ground, facing to the side all in the same direction (for example, everyone sits with their left shoulders toward the center of the circle.)

* The designated leader begins by putting their right hand over their heart center, and then places their left hand gently but firmly between the shoulder blades of the person sitting in front of them, and keeps it there. When that person feels the hand on their back, they repeat the sequence, placing their right hand over their heart center, and their left hand on the person in front. Repeat the sequence so that the touch travels all the way around the circle.

* Maintain the connection for a minute or two so that everyone has an opportunity to explore the experience somatically. The leader finishes the exercise by removing their hands and letting the disconnecting movement travel around the circle.

## Expressive Arts Experiments for Fire

* Draw a picture of the invisible flow of interpersonal energy that you experienced in any of the movement experiments above.
* Write a story about how your body felt the first time you fell in love. If that initial romantic experience included eventually getting burned, make that part of your story.

- In olden times, people would take a stone warmed by the fire to bed with them on cold nights. You can create your own version, by making a heating pad out of a small cloth bag filled with rice or wheat. Decorate the bag with symbols and colors that are evocative of the Element of Fire. To use the bag as a heating pad, microwave it on high for a minute or two until the dry grains inside become hot. (Make sure the materials you use to create the bag are microwave-safe.) The heating pad should retain its heat for up to an hour.

# Ether

Ether, the Element that is more than an Element, integrates the four Elements that precede it. It is the whole that is greater than the sum of its parts - an Elemental Gestalt. Alchemists refer to Ether as the Quintessence, the Fifth Element that simultaneously embodies the contradictory qualities of Earth, Water, Air, and Fire. Geometrically, it is the paradoxical center point, possessing both completeness and nothingness. An alchemical text describes it this way:

> *Reduce your stone to the four elements, rectify and combine them into one, and you will have the whole magistery. This One, to which the Elements must be reduced, is that little circle in the center of the squared figure. It is the mediator...*

> - John Opsopaus, The Rotation of the Elements, p. 6

We move toward a somatic quintessence by embodying the four Elements and refining our perception of them until we are able to experience our soma as a functional and dynamic whole. From a holistic or humanistic perspective, this implies the integration of body, mind, and spirit. From a Jungian perspective, Ether might be the individuated ability to access simultaneously the functions of thinking, feeling, intuition, and sensation (Opsopaus, 1995). For me, Ether is expressed in the ability to be grounded, fluid, inspired, and passionate in both intention and action.

It is important to emphasize that Ether's ability to integrate disparate parts and resolve polarities does not equate it with the Primal Chaos discussed in the section on Ancient Elements. The Prima Materia, or First Matter, is a chaotic but homogenized soup of unrealized potential in which polarities are neutralized. Ether is the refined integration of polarities that both realizes and transcends the potential suggested by the original chaos. Like the *Tao*, Ether is a paradox that is difficult to define precisely. It is the embodiment of all the Elements, yet it is not, itself, material.

In terms of somatic experience, the fact that Ether is not considered material may seem to present a quandary. How do we embody something that isn't there? The alchemical *Enigma of Hermes* expresses our somatic paradox with respect to attaining the Quintessence of the alchemist's art - "Unless you disembody the bodies and embody the disembodied, that which is expected will not take place." (Opsopaus, 1995. p. 5). This is echoed in the psychological cycling of the Elements described earlier by Von Franz (1980). The body is transformed into spirit, which then returns to the body, inspiriting it.

Rather than attempt to resolve the paradox, or enter into a lengthy philosophical discussion of the nature of the spirit (or the related debates about life after death or the existence of God, for example), my intention here is simply to offer some ideas developed over time, and to suggest ways to experience those ideas first-hand. The first of those ideas is expressed in the practice of contemplative movement. As discussed in the Introduction, movement as transcendent medium is an ancient tradition - human beings have been using movement as a method of embodying the spiritual dimension of life for thousands of years. Most early cultures show evidence of movement and dance as spiritual and religious expression (Blogg, 1988).

Defined simply, any movement of the body that reflects a deep communication with the spirit could be described as contemplative movement. This communication can take many forms, from a simple gesture, such as crossing oneself, to elaborate practices, such as the sequence of movements and postures in tai chi. Contemplative movement cannot, however, be defined by the visible outer movement alone. It can only be determined by the quality of inner connection the movement brings to the individual self. What occurs in contemplative movement often goes beyond the experience of self-connecting-with-self, however. Whether the movements are performed alone or as part of a group, the themes of transcendence and universal connection emerge as something that is being both sought and expressed.

On a more mundane level, I suggest that another template for exploring and understanding Ether is available to us anatomically, through the nervous system. The nervous system is one of the body s two major control systems, with the brain as its primary organ. The brain's cerebral cortex controls voluntary movement, sensory perception, language, personality, and the higher functions of thinking, memory, creativity and self-awareness. Below it lies the limbic system, which controls learning, motivation, and basic emotional expression. Tucked behind at the back of the head is the cerebellum, the area responsible for muscle tone, balance, posture, and skilled movement coordination. This central coordinating organ is linked to the rest of the body through a vast, complex series of nerve pathways that carry electrical impulses. This electricity, a nonmaterial physical phenomenon, is essential for animating and vitalizing the body.

Like Ether, the nervous system integrates. If the nervous system is fully developed, articulate, and responsive, the body and mind work as a seamless whole. Thinking, feeling, intuition, and sensation are coordinated with action. Inner experience and outer environment engage in a congruent dialogue. Not only is the nervous system actively involved in integrating different qualities, it is also capable of learning and dreaming. The capacity to transcend current somatic reality is inherent in the nervous system's structure and function. The Activating Experiments for Ether explore the nervous system's relationship to movement, and offer some ways to begin a more embodied dialogue with this ethereal body system.

## Somatic Reflections for Ether

On a somatic level, the Element of Ether is related to the embodied experience of the eternal, the infinite, the immaterial, and the universal. Although such abstract concepts might seem difficult to embody, we can begin to shift our somatic perspective toward an experience of those qualities. For example, Deepak Chopra (1989) offers an intriguing notion on the solidity of matter based on modern quantum physics; namely, that when understood on a subatomic level, over 96% of our physical body consists of empty space. Although our bodies are composed of over six trillion cells (Juhan, 1999), we are not solid entities by any means. On a fundamental level, neither are we temporal - since a basic law of physics states that matter can be neither created nor destroyed, the stuff of which we are made has been around forever. Although we may not ordinarily conceptualize ourselves this way, the Element of Ether allows us to encounter these basic truths of our corporeal existence. The first Somatic Reflection experiment is a somatic exploration of Chopra's notion of the spaciousness of matter. The second experiment touches on the Ether's shadow side, the existential abyss.

In these somatic reflections, and in the contemplative movement improvisations that follow, the somatic experience of silence and stillness is often figural. Michael Shea (1999, p. 28) describes the relationship of these qualities to the Ethereal expansion of awareness that accompanies deep somatic attentiveness:

> Somatic processes involve slowing down, waiting, and receiving the messages of my sensorium....Stillness will come to the foreground and becomes the strongest sensory experience. Interiority often shows us the chaos in our body. How often I forget that stillness and silence are always in the background. Stillness becomes dynamic when brought to the foreground of my somatic perception. It then becomes a strong sensory experience that widens my perception to include all other bodies as part of mine.

- With eyes closed, imagine the spaciousness within your body. Picture the inner space of your body as the whole universe - unlimited space and millions and millions of stars. Let the spaciousness within extend to the expansiveness of the universe. Allow inner space and outer space to become one experience.
- Imagine standing on a towering cliff at the edge of the world, with nothing but the abyss below and nothing but sky above

and before you. What is your somatic experience of/relationship with emptiness?

*"We are stardust...billion-year old carbon."*

*- Joni Mitchell, Woodstock, 1969*

## Activating Explorations for Ether

The nervous system plays an essential role in movement, and we can harness its ability to consciously affect the action and tone of the skeletal muscles. Voluntary movement requires an electrical impulse from the motor cortex of the frontal lobe to activate the muscle fibers. The skeletal muscles are enervated by a special type of nerve that, when it fires, initiates a contractile process in the muscle. The voluntary contraction of a muscle is produced by consciously activating the appropriate nerve pathways connected to the corresponding neurons. When the same movement is repeated, these nerve pathways are simplified and refined by the brain. These experiments work directly with the central nervous system to affect things like muscle tone and movement patterns.

### Mind/Matter in Motion

- Choose a muscle in your body that you would like to have feel more relaxed. With your eyes closed, imagine that muscle as slowly becoming warm and loose. You might imagine that the muscle is being gently massaged, or warmed in a sauna or whirlpool. You could also imagine that muscle as a lump of cold, hard butter that is slowly melting. When you open your eyes, notice how that muscle feels now. Note that since you did not physically warm or stretch the muscle, the changes you experience can be attributed solely to the activity of the nervous system stimulated by your intention.
- Find a movement that you would like to be able to do more effectively or comfortably. It might be swimming, or waltzing, or just walking across a room. Image yourself doing that

movement with grace and ease. Notice how your body responds as you visualize. Later, actually do that same movement. See what effect the imaging had on your experience.

## Integrating Inner/Outer

The nervous system is divided into the somatic and the autonomic nervous systems, which is further divided into the sympathetic and parasympathetic systems. The somatic nervous system is concerned with the processing of information related to inner functioning and to the external environment, and uses motor neurons to control skeletal muscle. The autonomic nervous system is concerned solely with internal functioning, and controls pulse rate, breathing, blood pressure and other vital functions. The parasympathetic system brings these body functions to a resting state conducive to digestion, and the sympathetic system does the opposite and prepares the body for action.

The somatic and autonomic nervous systems are often brought into active dialogue with each other by everyday situations. For example, you may have come down with the flu on the day of your driving exam. Your inner urge to stay home and rest reflects the efforts of the autonomic nervous system to bring the body towards a state of quiet conducive to healing. On the other hand, your external situation demands the mobilization of the somatic nervous system, in order to carry out the active processing required in driving a car. In this example, the demands of your inner situation (autonomic system) are in direct contrast to the demands of the external situation (somatic situation).

- Imagine some personal examples in which your somatic and autonomic nervous systems were called into conflict by the differing demands of a situation. Observe how your body responds as you image these situations. Do you follow the impulses of your body, or the demands of the environment? Although there is no one best way of responding, be aware of the choices you make in these situations.
- Now think of some instances in your life in which the autonomic and somatic systems were mobilized in same direction. (You are really tired, and get to sleep in as long as

you like...You just got a raise, and friends invite you out to celebrate.) Observe how your body responds as you image these situations.

## Expressive Improvisation for Ether

### Contemplative Movement

Find a quiet private space in which to move. Decide whether you want to work with or without music. If you already know music to be a source of spiritual inspiration, and have access to pieces that move you, music can provide both a stimulus and a loose structure for your movement. Working without music can provide a silence in which to listen to the movement impulses arising from your inner self.

- Make yourself comfortable - loose clothing, warmth, air, light, water - whatever you might need. You might want to do some gentle warm-up movements to ease your body into moving. You might also want to warm yourself up in other ways as well - through prayer, meditation, poetry, or song.
- When you feel prepared and focused, close your eyes, take a few full, easy breaths, and gradually allow yourself to attend within. Focus on your inner sense of how your body wants or needs to move. Allow the movements to develop naturally from within your own body, and give yourself permission to move however you want. The movements you make are not required to look beautiful to an outside observer. They will, however, often feel beautiful to you. Just keep letting yourself move, and be moved, as you focus on your inner sense of your spiritual self. One way to understand the essence of the movements you want to allow to surface is to ask yourself how your spirit would move if it could dance, or how your body would move if it were praying.
- Keep moving for as long as you feel moved to do so. Explore your sense of energy flow, connection, and expressiveness. Notice the effects of rhythm, repetition, intensity of movement, breathing, and movement quality. If you encounter inner resistance, and you have attended to whatever discomforts might be causing it, consider coming back to the movement at another time. These experiences

146

should be a pleasure, not a chore. You might still continue your contemplative explorations by reading, writing, prayer, meditation, or listening to music.

- When you are ready, allow your movement to come to a close. After you have finished moving, take a moment to breathe and feel your body. In particular, notice and feel your physical connection to the ground. Open your eyes slowly, and gently reorient yourself to your space. You might want to take a few moments for further reflection, or to record your experiences.

## Sufi Dancing

The best known contemplative movement tradition of the Muslim world comes, not from mainstream Islamic religious practice, but from the Sufi tradition. Sufism, although closely aligned with Islamic culture, is actually a distinct mystical, spiritual and philosophical school of thought. One Sufi order of monks, familiarly known as whirling dervishes, uses dance as a form of worship. The order was founded in the thirteenth century by a poet and mystic called Mevlana Jalalu ddin Rumi. The dervishes, dressed in long white robes and high hats or turbans, use several forms of dance as part of their religious rituals. In one of these dances, the dervishes revolve slowly for hours at a time. They dance on the spot, or move in large circles, with one hand held up to receive the blessings of God, and the other turned downward to send these blessings to the earth. As they turn, they transcend both exhaustion and dizziness to reach a heightened state of spiritual awareness (Murray, 1979). The dance best known through public performances by Sufi dervishes is the Dance of the Sama:

> The dervishes sit on sheepskins on the floor at equal distance from one another. Thus for half an hour - arms folded, eyes closed, head bowed - they remain in profound meditation. The sheikh, on a seat on a small carpet, breaks the silence by a hymn in honor of God. Then he invites the assembly to chant with him. (A description of the chant follows) This being ended, the dervishes, standing in line to the sheikhs left, arms folded, head bowed, slowly approach. The first

dervish, having arrived nearly opposite to the sheikh, profoundly salutes the tablet on which is inscribed the founder's name. Advancing by two leaps to the sheikh's side, he turns to him, salutes him, and begins to dance. The dance consists of turning on the left heel, advancing slowly, and making a turn of the hall with closed eyes and opened arms. This, in succession, all the dervishes do. Interrupted by two short pauses, during which the sheikh recites prayers, the dance lasts for two hours.

- *from a thirteenth century dervish text translated in 1891 by H.W. Clarke (Sufi Trust, 1980, p. 167)*

- Experiment with the Sufi form of contemplative movement using the description provided above. Begin by turning slowly for just a few minutes at a time until you have assessed your response to it in terms of balance and feelings of dizziness. If you have difficulty whirling with your eyes closed, keeping your eyes open but focused on the space within the reach of your arms may make it easier to maintain your equilibrium. Notice how you feel as you spin.

## Interactive Improvisation for Ether

You may extend the individual movement improvisation of contemplative movement to the interpersonal dimension by performing the movement experiment with others. I recommend that the experiment be done without music, and that each mover begin by attending only to their own movements initially. As each mover feels ready, they may slowly open their eyes just enough to begin safely moving through the room. As they become accustomed to the experience of attending within while simultaneously becoming aware of the presence of others, they may wish to open their eyes completely, and to begin to interact with other movers. If, at any point, it becomes difficult to retain the connection to the inner impulse to move, close your eyes and return to an inner focus until you again feel ready to expand your awareness to include others. Allow the group improvisation to come to a gradual close. When engaging in this type of movement experiment, I recommend that a trained facilitator be designated to act as silent witness to the group, and to signal the closing of the improv if necessary.

## Collective Movement Structures for Ether

### Spiral Dance

The spiral dance comes from the pagan Wiccan tradition, and embodies the spiral path of transcendence as the four Elements rotate toward the Ethereal center and then out again. This exercise is quoted from *The Spiral Dance* (Starhawk, 1989, p. 246):

> *The Spiral Dance can be another way to raise power. In a large group (at least thirty-five people and up to three or four hundred), begin in a circle with everyone facing in. The leader drops the hand of the person on her or his left, and begins moving toward the center in a clockwise direction.*
>
> *When the lead person nears the center of the circle, she/he turns toward her left hand, to face the person who is following her. (For simplicity's sake, let's assume the leader is a woman.) She keeps moving, always following her left hand. Each person in the spiral will pass all the other people in the group.*
>
> *Eventually, the leader will find herself outside the body of the spiral, facing out. She should continue about one quarter of the way around the outside edge and then turn again to face the person following her. She will then be leading the line around the outside of the circle, facing in.*
>
> *When she comes to a loop in the line, at the place where she turned, she goes inside the loop, and continues until she finds herself back in the center of the circle. Then she can wind the spiral tighter, letting the energy build and the chant become a wordless sound, until the group raises and grounds a cone of power.*

*This sounds horribly complicated but is actually easy
to do. Walk through it a few times first to gain
confidence. Be sure to go slowly, especially in a large
group, for if the leader goes too fast, the person at the
tail end of the line will be jerked around dangerously.*

The spiral dance is often accompanied by chanting or singing and drumming. The singing can have the effect of opening up a tight chest area through movement and sound resonance, while increasing the overall flow of oxygen to the body. The drumming provides a rhythmic anchor for the dancers to use to unify their movements, and can also serve as an almost hypnotic reference point for the consciousness of each dancer. Because of the inherent structure of the spiral dance, the experience of dancing it is one of multi-layered connection. Each dancer moving through the spiral will eventually meet, face to face, every other member of the dance. They do this while simultaneously being connected, through the chain of hands, to all the dancers at once. Dancers move through the experiences of being on the inside and on the outside of a group, and witness the paradox that one can be connected to someone who is moving in the opposite direction. The spiral dance is often used as an opening or closing ritual, and is usually imbedded in a larger religious context, such as celebrating a pagan festival or holy day (Starhawk, 1989).

## Integrating the Elements

This movement experiment uses individual movement expressions of the Elements in an integrative group format.

- Lie comfortably on the floor. Without consciously interfering with it, become aware of your breathing. Allow the awareness of your breath to guide your attention inwards to the bodily sensations and somatic awareness. Notice the different qualities of Earth, Water, Air, and Fire as you now embody them. Find the Element in your body you would most like to express.

- Slowly find a way to come to standing, keeping your eyes closed. Take a moment to breathe and get grounded and centered.
- Begin moving using just your hands, then expand your movement to include your arms, your head, then your whole body. Explore different movements until you find one that feels as though it expresses your somatic experience of the Element you have chosen. Allow a simple, repeatable movement to emerge.
- Share your Elemental movement signature with a partner. Teach it to them, and have them teach you their movement.
- The group begins by standing together in a circle. Each individual Elemental movement is danced by everyone in unison. Then each individual returns to their own Element. Without deliberate direction, allow these individual movements to evolve into a single collective group movement. Have everyone in the circle repeat this integrative movement together.

## Expressive Arts Experiments for Ether

- Draw a picture of your somatic experience of inner spaciousness in connection with the universe.
- Write a poem about your somatic experience of your nervous system.
- Write a story about your relationship with the existential abyss.
- Compose a song, chant, or mantra that, for you, integrates the essential qualities of the Elements.

The exercises and experiments in the preceding chapter offer a glimpse into the possibilities for using movement to embody the Elements and to effect somatic change. They are a starting point from which to begin a personal exploration into how you can experience and develop a relationship with these ancient cosmic building blocks on an internal, kinesthetic level. The next chapter describes the somatic experiences of seven individuals who engaged in a similar process to the one outlined in Embodied Elements. As participants in an introductory workshop in

Elemental Movement   , they recorded their impressions of the Elements through drawings, journal notes, and poetry.

# Embodying the Elements:

## Exploring Elemental Movement as a Somatic Model of Movement Education

## Abstract

This research study explores the effects of Elemental Movement , a somatic model of movement education. It employs an integrated feminist somatic research paradigm combined with a heuristic approach to presenting the research data. Seven practitioners of expressive arts therapy, movement education, or experiential psychotherapy participated in a two-day program of Elemental Movement . These co-researchers reported a variety of unique somatic, emotional, and psychological experiences in response to exploring the Elements through movement. The data generated was recorded by co-researchers through journal notes, poems, and drawings. The initial findings of this study suggest that movement is an effective medium for exploring a somatic relationship with the Elements, and that the Elements offer a useful framework and meaningful set of symbols for use in movement education.

## The Research Paradigm

Undertaking feminist somatic research in movement education requires that the researcher understand the research paradigms favored by several different disciplines, and be able to integrate them into a single coherent approach. The research, from topic selection through to design and evaluation, must reflect both feminist and somatic perspectives while effectively responding to the inherent challenges and requirements of the subject matter. Because a feminist somatic approach to research is not a model with which most readers will be familiar, a brief description of this approach is offered as a preface to the research report itself.

Although the importance of my feminist perspective to the development of Elemental Movement has been noted earlier in this manuscript, its influence on my approach to research requires further elaboration. Many of the somatic dimensions of the research process have already been articulated in the section on Somatic Alchemy, and will not be reiterated here except to offer some additional considerations with respect to types of research data and evaluation. Phenomenology is often the research model of choice for both feminist and somatic research (Johnson, 1999, and Cummerton, 1986), and some of its fundamental principles and processes will be included here as they have bearing on this particular study. The essential features of a heuristic research model will also be described. Although heuristic research stands as an independent paradigm and is not directly related to feminist or somatic research, it is being used as one of the conceptual and methodological foundations of this research project, especially with respect to data analysis. Lastly, some important considerations in researching movement-based phenomena will be addressed.

## Feminist Dimensions

Working with a holistic approach such as somatic movement education has important implications for the choice of research methodology. Anne Flynn, a feminist researcher in the Dance Department at the University of Calgary, explains the importance of a feminist approach to research in dance and movement. She notes that the dualistic concepts of body/mind, subjective/objective, science/art, emotion/reason, and female/male are deeply instilled within our traditional cultural view of the human being. Since dualism sets up exclusive either/or distinctions, the body and its movements continue to be symbolically (and often unconsciously) linked with nature, women, the subjective, the emotional, and the irrational, and *not* with mind, reason, or real objective knowledge (Tomm, 1989). Flynn asserts that the dualistic perspective of traditional research paradigms continues to separate mind and body in a manner that does not reflect the unified expression of self inherent in our movement. A feminist perspective, however, allows human movement to be studied without imposing false dichotomies or underrating the scientific value of the subject matter.

Feminist research draws upon a wide range of approaches, and each approach varies according to the views and subjects of the researcher. Each feminist researcher, in her own way, applies feminist perspectives, objectives, and values to research design and methodology. Despite the diversity of approaches used in feminist research, the principles of relationship, empowerment, and the validation of personal experience are incorporated into every aspect of the research process, transforming it in significant ways from more traditional models of scientific research (Cummerton, 1986). For example, in feminist research, theory often emerges from the research, rather than precedes it (Tomms, 1989). It is seen as one starting point from which to explore the many facets of experience, rather than an end point that proves or disproves a particular concept or belief. Although Elemental Movement is based on a theoretical framework drawn from an integration of somatic and alchemical theory, it is still in the process of being developed, clarified, and refined. To that end, this research project is intended primarily to generate new concepts, meanings, and information.

Several other aspects of this research study are informed by a feminist perspective. Like much feminist research, the method of data analysis is qualitative, and includes the personal documents of the co-researchers. In addition, group size ($n$) is based simply on the number of co-researchers needed to identify both diversity and similarity of experience (Cummerton, 1986). Embracing social diversity is one of the foundations of feminist thought, and a concerted effort was made to embody that principle in recruiting co-researchers for the study. Studies also show that feminist researchers are more likely to use non-experimental methods and to use co-researchers drawn from outside a university setting (Tomms, 1989). This research study is reflective of both those tendencies.

As a feminist researcher, my role is to provide information to the co-researchers about the research process itself, to act as a facilitator of the research process, and to encourage and allow a wide range of responses to the issue being studied (Cummerton,

1986).  Unusual, unexpected, or complex findings are valued for their ability to generate new ideas and questions into the nature of the issue being studied.  In contrast to traditional research, in feminist research my personal values and experiences are articulated and included in the research process.  I include a description of my involvement in the research study, explain my bias and value stance, and describe my personal and professional experience related to the issue being studied.  Because I regard my co-researchers as experts of their own experience, and understand that the opportunity to communicate that experience often has more value for them than pleasing the researcher, I feel I can be more comfortable taking the risk of enhancing the demand characteristics by disclosing my values.  Co-researchers collaborate actively in the research, and use the researcher as an informed guide and resource.  They are participants in the true sense of the word, rather than merely objects of research.  Co-researchers are also capable of providing valuable insight into their experience, and this research study encourages them to evaluate their own experience, rather than having a designated expert evaluate it for them.

In evaluating the results of research, feminist researchers also stress the importance of describing multi-causal interdependent factors, rather than attempting to isolate single causes (Tomms, 1989).  The criteria of validity of feminist research is based on completeness, illustrativeness, understanding, and responsiveness to readers and co-researchers' experience (Cummerton, 1986), and this study is oriented toward meeting those criteria.

## Somatic Implications

Thomas Hanna, in his article, *What Is Somatics?* (1986-87), outlines a perspective on researching human experience that departs from traditional paradigms in one crucial aspect.  He suggests that a categorical distinction needs to be made between the data available from an objective third-person perspective, and the data obtainable from a first-person perspective.  Offering examples from physiology, psychology, and medicine, he argues that because research in these fields has traditionally ignored subjective data, the results of that research are incomplete. Objective analysis includes only data that supports the view of the human body as an object. In contrast, when the human being is approached from a first-person viewpoint, an intrinsically different set of data is observed.

It is important to emphasize that the difference between objective and subjective data is one of type rather than degree of accuracy or value. These two separate modes of investigating human experience are irreducible and coequal. However, the fact that traditional research approaches in the life sciences have largely ignored subjective data calls into question the validity of their results. Hanna suggests that science has validity in both its research and theory only to the degree that all data are considered, and to ignore or avoid evidence that is "phenomenological" or "subjective" is unscientific. Like a feminist approach, a somatic approach to research values and strives to include both subjective and objective data, and to represent human experience as multi-dimensional. This research study attempts to include data from a variety of sources and perspectives.

Another important consideration in conducting research from a somatic perspective concerns the nature of the subject being studied. Human beings are not merely complicated objects - we are self-aware subjects. As such, we change constantly throughout, and in response to, the process of being observed. Our awareness of ourselves and our environment is continually being updated, and because our sensory system operates in tandem with our motor system, we act (even if imperceptibly) on all our sensory impressions (Hanna, 1986). This on-going process of self-regulation means that it is unrealistic to research human experience as if it were a static event, or even an event that could be fully represented by examining a set of before-and-after assessment measures. This research study acknowledges an understanding of the somatic processes inherent in human experience, and recognizes that the changes reported in the individuals being studied are only fragmentary snapshots in a constantly evolving process of change.

# Influence of Phenomenology

A phenomenological approach does not denote any particular method, but rather refers to research that is conducted in adherence to the philosophy of phenomenology -- i.e., that it seeks to understand the meaning of subjective experience. Much of the research conducted into somatic disciplines is based on a phenomenological approach, and the recently published *Encyclopedia of Phenomenology* contains an entry acknowledging the significance to phenomenology of somatic research (Johnson, 1999). Phenomenologist Elizabeth Behnke, in describing the challenges of communicating somatic experiences, ideas, or techniques, emphasizes the importance of "cashing in" the description by actually trying out in one's own body the material being described (Johnson, 1996). She considers this translation into direct experiential evidence to be one of the cornerstones of Husserlian phenomenology. In my view, the implications of this idea, especially with respect to research reporting and evaluation, are significant. Rather than simply sketching the broad outlines of the research process in the report, the activities need to be described in enough detail for each and every reader of the report to replicate an analogous experience. Evaluation and external validation can proceed from the same assumption, and through the same process - the research is reported in way that makes it possible for it to be duplicated, evaluated, and validated one soma at a time. For that reason, this research report is prefaced by sections in the book that describe in detail each of the somatic and movement experiments used in the course of the study.

# Influence of Heuristic Concepts and Methodology

Heuristic research refers to a process of internal investigation through which one discovers the nature and meaning of a particular human experience, and develops methods and procedures for further investigation. A heuristic paradigm shares some important features with a phenomenological research approach, while also possessing some important distinctions (Moustakas, 1990). Several of these differences are important to our discussion here, as they are also strongly congruent with feminist principles and objectives. Heuristic inquiry actively emphasizes connection and relationship with the subject matter being researched, in contrast to the relative detachment encouraged by a phenomenological approach. In the case of Elemental Movement , I am deeply involved as both researcher and developer. This model of movement education evolved out of a lengthy personal exploration of how the Elements might be embodied through movement, and the study was constructed through the same process of internal investigation - trying out in my own body first what might also serve as a catalyst for the explorations of others.

Where phenomenology permits the researcher to offer definitive descriptions of experience, heuristic researchers attempt to portray the personal significance and essential meanings of experience. In describing that experience, heuristic research retains the visibility of research participants, rather than losing them as individual persons in the process of descriptive analysis. This emphasis on connection and personal experience echoes the feminist concern for valuing research participants as real people. In an effort to embody this value, this research study presents the data as portraits of individual experience, drawing on their own artistic expressions to illustrate and illuminate it.

Heuristic research also offers a process remarkably similar to the alchemical process of individuation and integration described in earlier chapters. Rather than dissecting experience and leaving it in abstracted pieces, the heuristic method attempts to recreate lived experience in a process that "moves from whole to part and back to whole again" (Moustakas, 1990, p. 16). Beginning with initial engagement, immersion in the subject, and allowing time for incubation, the research then moves towards illumination and explication, culminating in a creative synthesis. This final stage of creative synthesis could be likened to the Elemental and alchemical step of integration. Like Ether, it requires the separation, distillation, and reintegration of the essential elements of experience into a whole that is greater than the sum of its parts.

# Considerations for Research in Movement Education

Movement education presents several unique challenges for the researcher, on both practical and theoretical levels. Because movement is a non-verbal medium, translating non-verbal data into accurate and illuminating textual data can be a difficult task, but one that is often essential to making the research data understandable. Another important challenge arises out of attempting to describe the effects of an inherently holistic treatment approach to an audience that employs a largely dualistic theoretical framework for understanding behavioral research results. More specifically, somatic movement education makes no distinction between what is body and what is mind - it is understood that movement possesses physical, emotional, psychological, and social dimensions that do not need to be separated from one another in order to be known. In contrast, traditional behavioral research still seeks to understand human behavior as belonging predominantly to one dimension or another. In very simple terms, most traditional academic audiences will want to understand the research results in terms of, You did something with their bodies, and that had a beneficial effect on their minds... or You did something with their minds, and that had a beneficial effect on their bodies... , when the movement education researcher sees the process as We did something with our body/minds that had an effect on our body/minds. By presenting *verbatim* much of the data generated by co-researchers, it is hoped that this dynamic inter-relationship of body and mind will be evident.

The Committee on Research in Dance has articulated similar problems with research in dance/movement therapy (CODA, 1970). They also note that human movement is culturally loaded , and that the definition of normal movement patterns or abilities is culturally relative. As well, movement content is not always congruent with verbal content, so accurately assessing a movement s meaning can be problematic. For this reason, the research study emphasizes using the co-researcher's own assessment of the meaning of their movement.

## Summary

An integrated feminist somatic approach lends itself to research in movement education for a number of reasons. Perhaps the most significant is laid out by Anne Flynn in her description of how inappropriate a traditional dualistic research methodology would be. A feminist somatic approach can also address the problems raised by the Committee on Research in Dance. For example, the feminist practice of articulating bias, including cultural bias, as part of the research process, acknowledges the cultural relativity of movement. A phenomenological approach has already been adopted by many feminist and somatic researchers, and lends itself to the exploration of meaning so fundamental to the study of subjective experience. Having co-researchers observe and provide reflective assessments of their own movement empowers them as experts on their own experience and allows them to assign meanings to those movements informed by somatic knowledge. Integrating feminist and somatic principles with heuristic concepts and methodology reinforces the values of personal connection, integrity, and authenticity. A heuristic paradigm also offers a research process congruent with the methodology employed in the practice of Elemental Movement itself.

By integrating compatible aspects of feminist, somatic, phenomenological, and heuristic research, it is possible to create a preliminary model of an integrated research paradigm suitable for investigating the experience of Elemental Movement . It is also my hope that this integrated model may be of use to other researchers in the ongoing development of a somatic research paradigm.

# The Research Question

At the heart of this research study lies the central question of how Elemental Movement is experienced somatically by those who engage in it. The experiments and procedures utilized in this study are designed to explore, illuminate, and illustrate the subjective perceptions of co-researchers as they participate in an intensive introductory experience of Elemental Movement . This fundamental research question - "What are the somatic effects of Elemental Movement ?" - arises out of an earlier questioning on the part of the researcher that has been described in more detail in a previous chapter. It integrates the alchemical idea that everything in the universe, including my own body, is composed of five essential Elements, with the somatic notion that it is possible to explore and understand my inner experience through kinesthetic awareness. By combining this basic notion of somatic theory with the basic notion of alchemical and elemental theory, one arrives at the question, "How are the Elements embodied?", and, more personally, "How do I embody the Elements?" Elemental Movement was developed in response to this initial question, as a way to explore and begin to answer it.

The general question of this research is both substantive and theoretical in nature - it is related to the specific issue of the somatic effects of Elemental Movement , but it is also tied to broader theoretical issues such as the nature of somatic change, and the role of the body in creative expression. Although the purpose of this research project is to explore the effects of a particular model of somatic movement education, it is hoped that the study will also contribute to an increased understanding of the somatic effects of movement education in general. Because of the integrative and multidisciplinary nature of Elemental Movement , research into its effects could also have an impact on developments in the modern field of alchemy, as well as the psychotherapeutic dimensions of dance and movement as expressive arts.

## Review of the Literature

Because Elemental Movement is a newly developed model of somatic movement education, there have been no previous formal attempts to research its effects. Related historical investigations into the nature of the embodied Elements, and the use of alchemical symbolism in transforming somatic experience have been described in earlier chapters on the Ancient Elements and Inner Alchemy. Although several research studies and Ph.D.

theses on alchemy exist in the literature[24], none deal specifically with the Elements or with movement. Most focus on alchemical symbolism in works of literature and art (MacLean, 1999). Similarly, a review of the research into somatic education and dance/movement therapy[25] reveals no previous articles or studies involving alchemy or the Elements as symbols or instruments.

# Methodology

## Research Design

### Design.

A feminist somatic research paradigm combined with a heuristic research approach to data analysis was employed for the study. Co-researchers for the study were self-selected.

### Procedure.

Co-researchers engaged in a two-day group program of Elemental Movement . Prior to the study, co-researchers met with the primary researcher to discuss the objectives of the study as well as their hopes, concerns, and expectations with respect to their participation. The Elemental Movement model was explained, and a manual containing a description of the background, theory, structure, and content of the model was provided. Directly prior to the program, they attended a group orientation session in which they were provided with further information about the program and the research process, met their fellow co-researchers, and completed the first Elemental Body

---

[24] Based on a database of graduate theses and doctoral dissertations on alchemy through the Alchemy Virtual Library. To my knowledge, this does not include material in the archives of the C.G. Jung Institutes in Zurich or New York.

[25] Based on a review of the following databases: Networked Digital Library of Theses and Dissertations (NDLTD), Academic Search Elite, ERIC, PsycINFO, and Sociofile, which includes the Somatics Journal and the Journal of Dance/Movement Therapy.

Map[26].   Co-researchers were also offered guidelines for safe participation and definitions of key terms used during the study.

The two-day program was divided into equal sections devoted to the exploration of each of the five Elements, beginning with Earth and moving through Water, Air, and Fire, to finish with Ether. The program was designed so examples of most of the five steps of Elemental Movement - Activation, Expression, Interaction, etc. - were included for each Element. The movement experiments conducted during the two-day program are as follows, and are described in detail in the section on Embodied Elements.

**Earth** - Gravity Connection, Earth Walk, Dancing from the Bones and Organs, and Body Rhythms.

**Water** - Inner Water, Waves and Tides, Bodypainting, and Kinesthetic Reflections.

**Air** - Dimensional Breath, Exploring the Kinesphere, and Dancing on Air (both individual and interactive versions).

**Fire** - Pulsing Warmth, Energy Flow, Sensory Dimensions of Fire, and Fire Dance.

**Ether** - Somatic Reflections for Ether, Sufi Dancing, Integrating the Elements.

Each individual movement experiment was followed by time for the co-researchers to process and record their experiences - sometimes the processing was facilitated through group discussion, and at other times individually through a series of questions offered by the facilitator. Co-researchers were free to record their experiences any way they chose, and additional suggestions for documentation were made by the facilitator for most of the exercises. At the end of the two-day program, a final Elemental Body Map was completed, and co-researchers were debriefed as a group.

---

[26] The Elemental Body Map is a drawing created in response to a guided somatic awareness exercise, and contained graphic representations of where and how the Elements were experienced somatically. This guided exercise and the specific somatic experiments employed in the study are described in detail in the preceding section on the Embodied Elements.

# Population and Setting

## Primary Researcher Attributes.

Many of the professional perspectives and preferences of the primary researcher have been articulated in previous sections of the text, notably in the preface to the section on Somatic Alchemy describing Elemental Movement 's theoretical framework. My life experience and personal attributes also color the nature of the research in less obvious, but equally significant, ways. Being a white, urban, Western-educated, poor, able-bodied, bisexual female affects my presence in the world, and the world's response to me. So does being calm, gentle, (usually) organized, and (often) funny. The personal qualities I bring to any relationship dynamic necessarily include my relationship with the co-researchers in this study. My assumption is that who I am as a person affects my co-researchers, and vice versa. The dynamics of our interpersonal interactions influence our somatic experiences. Since the data describes somatic experience, our relational encounters are reflected in it.

## The Role and Participation of Primary Researcher.

Undertaking the role of primary researcher influenced many of the choices I made in the development and implementation of this study. For example, in structuring the program, I selected experiments intended for high-functioning, experienced, relatively sophisticated participants, and placed less emphasis on group building, verbal processing, and group dynamics than I would if planning a program designed for personal development in the general population.

As primary researcher/facilitator in this study, I also made important choices about how (and how much) to respond in the moment to the vivid and fertile material generated by co-researchers over the course of the program. These choices were different from the ones I would have made if my main role had been one of therapist/facilitator. As a rule, I chose not pursue the oppportunities I observed for further developing the psychological content of the material produced by co-researchers, and to offer instead a container for holding and grounding the responses generated by the movement experiments[27].

My active participation in the Elemental Movement program itself was limited mostly to group movement improvisation experiments and general group discussions. For the most part, my role was to guide the exercises, stimulate reflection and discussion, and observe co-researchers' responses.

## Co-researcher Attributes.

Co-researchers in the study consist of practitioners in expressive arts therapy, experiential psychotherapy, and/or somatic movement therapy. Beyond that similarity, and the fact that each co-researcher brings a wealth of personal and professional experience to bear on the research, the group is diverse. Traditional methods of depicting the demographics of a research group assume that the criteria selected for use in describing these individuals is valid and relevant both to the readership and to the individuals involved. It presumes, for example, that characterizing someone in terms of their age, gender, race, etc., accurately represents who they are. As a feminist, I believe this approach simply imposes another type of uniformity while attempting to describe diversity. Since this research study attempts to honor the uniqueness of the co-researchers experience, individual profiles of each co-researcher preface the description of their experience. These profiles were written by the co-researchers using criteria meaningful for them. (See Appendix Four for a copy of the Participant Bio sheet completed by co-researchers.)

## The Role and Participation of Co-researchers.

In keeping with feminist and heuristic research values (Moustakas, 1990, and Tomms, 1989), the co-researchers were

---

[27] The containment and grounding functions of my role as facilitator were implemented through regularly orienting participants to the present environment and to their own sensory awareness. Examples of these interventions are included in the Emotional Safety Kit on Page 97 as well as in the Research Information Package offered to co-researchers.

informed as much as possible with respect to the nature of the research design, its purpose and process, and their role in the research. Each prospective participant in the study was interviewed individually, and given a Research Study Information package, which is included here as Appendix Three. To facilitate their active collaboration, a copy of the Elemental Movement program to be used in the study was also provided to co-researchers prior to the study itself.

**Risks and Benefits of Participation:** The study did not involve the deliberate imposition of any stress on co-researchers. The physical stresses of movement education are minimal, and were minimized further by the participation guidelines and by the exercise safety knowledge of the facilitator. The program involves a moderate amount of physical activity, but all guided exercises are designed to be safe, and the risks of physical harm anticipated in the research were no greater than those ordinarily encountered in the performance of routine physical activities. In addition, all co-researchers were required to complete a Physical Activity Readiness Questionnaire as part of the consent form, in order to screen out those for whom even mild exercise might be medically inadvisable. The anticipated psychological stresses were also low. Although opportunities to encounter, explore and reveal material of a personal nature did arise over the course of the program, the potential risks associated with these types of experience were be minimized. The program structure emphasizes safety in interactions and experiences, and the facilitator is trained to recognize and address potential difficulties before they can detract from a positive experience. Because co-researchers will already have undergone some professional-level training requiring personal exploration, it was not expected that they would encounter unforeseen emotional or psychological difficulty as a result of their participation. Individuals who were currently in emotional or psychological crisis were not knowingly be accepted as research co-researchers. As an additional safeguard, program co-researchers were required to have access to psychotherapeutic resources during and immediately following the study.

**Privacy:** Co-researchers were not asked to reveal anything of a personal nature unless they wished to do so. The submission of any and all self-observations (i.e. journal notes, artwork, etc.) over the course of the program for use as research data was voluntary.

**Anonymity:** Only first names or pseudonyms were used in the research report.

**Confidentiality:** Co-researchers were instructed not to discuss the identity or experiences of fellow co-researchers without their expressed consent at any time during or following the study. Original copies of raw data generated by program co-researchers were returned to them following the completion of the research report. Photographs and photocopies of the raw data designated for use in the research report were securely stored, accessible only to the researcher. Researcher copies of any data not used in the research report were destroyed upon final acceptance of the report by the researcher's Independent Study Advisory Committee.

**Measures taken to enable subjects to omit specific procedures or terminate participation:** Guidelines for participation were communicated to co-researchers both verbally and in writing prior to commencement of the study. These guidelines include the following information: 1) Co-researchers are encouraged to participate in only the activities they choose, 2) Co-researchers are encouraged to adapt procedures or activities to accommodate their own personal preferences, and 3) Co-researchers may withdraw from the study at any time, for any reason, without fear of reproach. If a co-researcher withdraws from the study, any information collected from them will be deleted from the research materials.

## Setting.

The research was conducted in a private community center rented for the purpose of the study. It was chosen for its physical properties (space, light, good flooring, and access to fresh air), as well as for its relative lack of associations to clinical research, dance or physical education.

## Data Collection

### Materials.

One of the tools employed to help co-researchers depict and evaluate their overall experience was an Elemental Body Map, drawn by co-researchers in response to a guided visualization exercise led by the researcher at the start of the program. The full text of this exercise is included at the beginning of the Embodied Elements section. After completing a second Body Map at the end of the program, co-researchers were asked to describe the changes they experienced as a result of their participation in the Elemental Movement program. In addition to being asked to evaluate their personal experience, they were also asked to evaluate the Elemental Movement model based on their experience. (See Appendix Four for copies of the Evaluation questions.)

### Additional Techniques.

Additional data-collection techniques used in the study consisted of co-researcher and facilitator self-observation recorded at regular intervals throughout the program. These self-observations took the form of drawings, journal notes, poems, and verbal responses to guided discussion. Some of the questions upon which these self-observations were based include, "What are you aware of experiencing in your body at this moment?" and "How would you describe or express the quality of sensation you are currently experiencing?" Photographs were also taken throughout the program, and are included in the text of the report.

## Presentation of the Data

Somatic experiments are similar to chemical reactions, although they differ in degree of complexity. Because the program of Elemental Movement being researched in this study is composed of a series of over 20 individually complex somatic experiments, numerous variables are involved, and many data points are produced. Despite a cultural bias toward experiments with simple variables and quantitatively defined data, it is not possible to evaluate somatic experiments without embracing complexity and subjectivity. For this reason, I have chosen to employ a method of data analysis based on heuristic research, which includes depictions of each individual's experience as well as of the experience as a whole. Verbatim examples and illustrations are also included. The results of the study conclude with a creative synthesis of the data by the primary researcher.

The personal profile that prefaces each individual co-researcher's depiction is italicized to distinguish it from the main description. These profiles were provided by the co-researchers themselves. The main descriptive passages were taken directly from the co-researcher's notes, and then edited by the primary researcher for clarity and brevity. The primary researcher also selected one or two drawings from each co-researcher's materials to illustrate their written material. These edited "thumbnail sketches" were then reviewed by the individual co-researcher, to ensure that these condensed editions accurately and expressively reflected their experiences. The initial versions were unanimously approved by co-researchers, with the exception of a minor change in one profile.

## Glenmore

*Glenmore describes himself as someone who laughs, cries, expresses anger, makes love/sex, and looks forward to experiencing all of these more. He feels blessed with good health, work, friends, family, and a spiritual path. He often feels younger on the inside than he does on the outside. He would like to meet someone he is genetically connected to.*

The drawing in Figure 5 represents the Elemental Body Map created by Glenmore at the beginning of the program. The back surface of his body is connected to Earth, and feels cool and firm. Water is flexible, and is found in the body in sacs, like water balloons. Air is contained in the thin black outline just below the surface of his skin, and feels safe and contained. Fire jumps from the surface of his body, and is the integrating force that creates Ether.

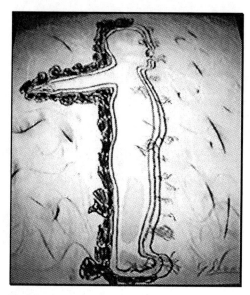

*Figure 5*

In exploring the Element of Earth further, Glenmore discovers good, heavy, solid feelings throughout his body. He is also aware of some anxiety about being unable to escape from Earth. When he shifts his relationship to gravity to one that feels more interactive and reciprocal, the anxiety diminishes. Earth alters Glenmore's bodily sense of time, and things feel slower.

The movement explorations of the Element of Water mark a shift in the bodily perception of weight. For Glenmore, Water is pale blue and shimmering, and he experiences a desire to just float in its gentle womb-like support.. He writes the following poem about Water:

> *A drunken, lost, reluctant sailor*
> *Head swimming in murky unscary depths*
> *Gently starts swimming out to sea*
> *Ever farther from the shore, to deeper and deeper*
> *waters*
> *Still unafraid.*

*Perhaps wishing to finally surrender and be forever lost*

-

*Or forever found!*
*In the soothing, turbulent, purifying abyss*
*That started with but a few clear drops from heaven.*


On a body level, Air is a familiar Element for Glenmore - he acknowledges his breath often throughout the day. In the Air explorations, he experiences a profound sense of calm and relaxation. He enjoys the space inside himself, and connects to a sense of expansion and openness.

In contrast, exploring the Element of Fire evokes a sense of excitement and risk. The drawing in Figure 6 represents Glenmore's inner experience of Fire during the Somatic Meditation. During an expressive movement exploration, he plays with finding a balance between the cool, black space and the warm, passionate flames of embodied energy. He discovers that connecting with others from this experience of Fire energy is a new place of contact, and feels both excited and shaky about taking that risk.

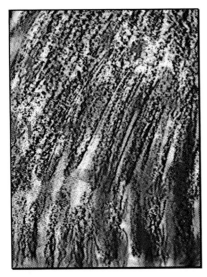

*Figure 6*

At the beginning of the program, Glenmore expressed a particular interest in discovering more about his embodied experience of Ether. He expresses his findings in this poem:

*Internalized infinity*
*Contained, bound by ageless existence*
*As if the infinite can be bound*
*As if eternity can be only internalized*
*Perhaps now there is comfort in this imagining*
*Perhaps one day I will not need the comfort/safety*
*of these images to experience infinity and eternity*
*My infinity, my eternity*
*Me as infinity, me as eternity*
*I infinity, I eternity.*


In evaluating his experience of embodying the Elements, Glenmore describes himself as possessing a greater awareness of and pleasure in how the elements exist and are expressed within him - physically, emotionally, cognitively and spiritually. He appreciated the opportunity to explore the "shadow" sides of the Elements in an "unheavy", positive way. He is also excited about an enhanced experiential awareness of how polarities exist and work together. He feels as though exploring the Elements has great healing and therapeutic benefit for him, and is looking forward to ongoing exploration. In particular, he is interested in learning how to integrate his experience of the Elements into other contexts.

Figure 7

## Pam

*Pam is a 29-year-old, white, middle-class, Jewish female. She is a psychotherapist and bodyworker.*

Pam's experience of embodying the Element of Earth possesses a range of qualities. In the Somatic Meditation, she finds that it feels good to let go into the Earth and feel it pushing up to meet her body. She experiences the Earth in this way as supportive and holding. Exploring her skeleton and organs through movement, she finds dancing from the bones free and flowing with a staccato feel. In contrast, her organ dance is more rounded, internal, and sensual.

Embodying the Element of Water evokes soft, luxuriant qualities for Pam, and inspires a poem that suggests the nurturing, primal dimensions of Water:

*Water Dance*
*baby baby oh so green*
*curled up fingers and toes*
*eyes yet to open*

174

*a first step, an initiation*
*one two three four five*
*I can move these fingers*
*look, see how I make them move*
*open open to you*
*behind, in front*
*up up up they go*
*and around*
*and around like butterflies*
*swimming and flying*
*aha they are mine and they move so well*

*Figure 8*

The Element of Air possesses contrasting dimensions for Pam. On one hand, she enjoys exploring the Air in the space around her, and feeling as though she could claim the space around her as her own. On an internal level, however, Air as breath is both a comfort and a discomfort. Pam discovers that rhythmic breathing evokes emotion, and that she can feel "spacey" when surrounded by too much Air. The embodiment of the Element of Fire is expressed for Pam through the drawing in Figure 8.

The Somatic Meditation for the Element of Ether stimulates an out-of-body sensation for Pam - a light, spacey, timeless experience that she wants to remain in "for eternity". In contrast, the collective movement exploration for Ether - Sufi-inspired dancing - evokes feelings of dizziness and fatigue. Pam wonders if the spinning motion might have shaken her up emotionally, as she feels like having a good cry afterwards.

In evaluating her experience of embodying the Elements over the course of the weekend, Pam feels as though she is taking away a full experience. She has a deeper experiential understanding of how she connects with the Elements on both an internal and external level. She is also aware of how this experience has opened up a range of possibilities for further explorations and connections with the Elements. Her final Elemental Body Map of all the Elements integrated is included here in Figure 9.

*Figure 9*

*Figure 10*

## Maura

*Maura is a white middle-class woman in her late twenties who works as a feminist counselor and teaches expressive dance to women. She came to explore dance through her own healing process in her late teens. She believes dance is a healing path and expresses the connection between art and healing, Self and Spirit in her life and work. She began to investigate the elements through dance and ritual a few years ago and finds they hold new teachings each time she revisits them.*

The two Elemental Body Maps on the following pages represent the front and back of Maura's body as she engaged in the initial mapping of how she experiences the Elements. The Earth element (Figure 12) is experienced in the back of her body as heavy, sinking, and pulled by gravity. The experience of Water is a relief after the heaviness of Earth, and Air evokes a light, tingly, slightly scary sensation, as if she might fly out the front of her body. Fire (Figure 11) is experienced in her belly, hands, and legs as desire, hunger, anger, and energy. In contrast, Ether is experienced as a spiritual rather than sensual. Maura feels it as an energy field lining the body, as well as in the eyes, throat, top of head, and forehead.

177

Further explorations of the Element of Earth reveal a connection with it as Mother, and as a living presence. Maura describes feeling deeply loved by the Earth, as well as feeling its pain. Connection with Earth reminds her of her purpose on the planet, and reconnects her with her soul. She describes the loose, strong, heavy dance of walking on the Earth as an interaction between her and Mother Earth.

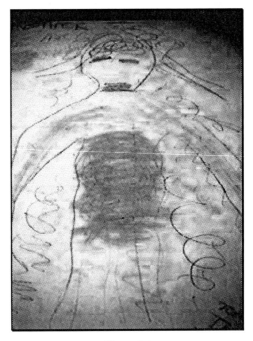

*Figure 11*

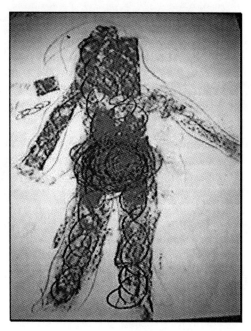

*Figure 12*

Water also evokes a sense of feminine presence for Maura. She writes the following poem in response to movement explorations of Water:

> *The pregnant moon yearns to give birth to her fullness*
> *She reflects the water cycles - Maiden, Mother, Crone.*
> *Tonight, sisters, she is a full cup.*
> *"Oh, Water, " she pleads, " Reflecting fecund form,*
> *mirror my voluptuous round body*
> *so that I can be empty again."*
> *Stars form an umbilical cord.*
> *Water child is born.*

The theme of birth is echoed in a second entry for Water:

> *I cried as the tide rolled in*
> *Standing beside the ever-changing ocean*
> *I sang a song for those who lost their souls to the sea*
> *I looked into their faces, frozen expressions bobbing*
> *through patches of cool seaweed and foam.*

*Hollow heads ripple across the moonlight shimmering
wake.*
*Each are looking for a body home*
*Here is where they come to be reborn - searching for
form*
*Here they find only the murky fluidity of water.*


The movement explorations for the Element of Air suggest a relationship with a more masculine presence, as Maura writes of exploring the space around her as "hands marry Sky, moving through his spacious body." The floating, flying sensation of Air evokes both feelings of celestial connection and fearlessness as well as a longing to return to the Earth and away from the place "where the soul escapes the body".

Ether also inspires an experience of relationship for Maura, this time in response to the movement of whirling.

<u>Body Opens To Spirit</u>

*Magician come to me wearing your magic twirling
cape of silver and gold*
*Take me inside the Infinity, your coat of spaceless
wonder*
*There we will spin and spiral, whirl and twirl as the
dervish.*
*Time vanishes, sky thins, earth beneath the feet
becomes formless*
*and the universe above and below dissolves*
*I feel with this dance you are my timeless lover*
*bringing me home to Now.*

Several awarenesses arise for Maura as she evaluates her experience of Elemental Movement. The first is that she would have liked more time to explore each Element further. Although she has explored the Elements through movement before, this experience unearths some new material for her. The second has to do with her response to the movement explorations for Water and Air. She notes that her experience of Air surprised her in how ungrounded she felt in it, and wonders if leaving some emotional

Water material unexplored may have affected her ability to move fully into the next Element.

## Iesha

Figure 13

*Iesha is a 26-year-old black woman of African and Caribbean descent. Her academic, professional, and work backgrounds all focus on issues pertaining to cross-cultural, feminist epistemologies and perspectives to self, community and international development through the use of anti-oppression initiatives, the arts, politics and other healing tools. Presently, she is co-facilitating expressive art groups for women and children survivors of violence/trauma and pursuing additional academic training.*

*Elementally Me*

*Blackness Grips*
*Her Feet*
*Rooted In The*
*Brownish Red*
*Soul Of Her Life.*
*Her Soil*
*Strengthens*
*Sturdying Her Body*
*Playing The Balancing Game*
*With Mother Earth*
*Persevering.*
*The Foundation*
*Quickly Floating*
*In Mossy Green Waters*
*Opening Her Insides*
*Drowning Her Numbness*
*Her Silence*

181

*Purifying Her Pursuit*
*Tickling Survival*
*And Challenging*
*Emotions Not To Close*
*Struggling*
*Stomach Memories*
*Explosions Of Colours*
*Orange, Red*
*Surrounding Her Heart*
*Pumping Passion*
*Creating Rational Confusion*
*Awakening The Fire Within*
*The Paradox*
*Candles Comfort And Soothe*
*Irrational Thoughts*
*Flames Circle*
*Flickering*
*Knowledge*
*Inside Her Head*
*Contrasting Identities...*
*Stretching Beyond*
*Blue Imagination*
*Embracing Creativity*
*Painting The Sky*
*With Spirited Expressions*
*Dreaming*
*Healing Through Air*
*Entering The Yellow Gates*
*Of The Unknown*
*Choosing Present Paths*
*Guided By Future Choices*
*And Past Decisions*
*Energizing*
*Purple Light*
*Deep*
*Within Her Body*
*Journeying*
*Through Mind*
*Discovering Soul*
*Finding Her Ether Tree.*

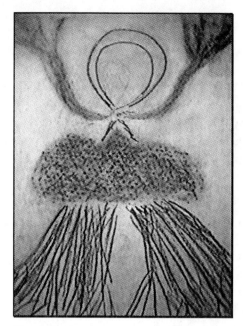

*Figure 14*

The drawing and poem in Figure 14 illustrate Iesha's response to encountering all the Elements on a body level. Explorations of each individual Element evoke additional responses - Earth is connected to feelings of being grounded as well as to associations with ancestors, tradition, and the struggle for freedom. Water reminds Iesha of birth, and the struggle to breathe - she describes the sensation as one of being born drowning. The embodied Element of Water is also waves of emotion stuck in her stomach that she struggles to calm. In contrast, Air is about creating expression, light, sound, and energy. Fire explorations create associations both to cool passion and hot compassion, and elicit the drawing in Figure 15. Ether is the unknown Element for Iesha, and she describes her experience of it in terms that embody polarities such as light and darkness, fear and safety, and falling and support.

In evaluating her experience of embodying the Elements through movement, Iesha notes how expression through movement can have such power without words. She would like to explore the element of Water more fully at some point, as she realizes its connection to deep emotion for her. Although she describes herself as taking away the gift of movement and the awareness of how the Elements affect her daily experience, Iesha also emphasizes the need to continue to process her experience in order to evaluate it as deeply as she feels it went.

*Figure 15*

*Figure 16*

## Peter

     *Peter describes himself as a 43-year-old Peter Pan who is also a Fire monkey and an Earth Taurus. He is a therapeutic recreation/stress management therapist, a Trager practitioner, a body-centered therapist, and a specialized kinesiologist. For nine years, he played bass trombone with the Hong Kong Philharmonic.*

*Figure 17*

The drawing in Figure 17 represents Peter's expression of the five Elements as he experiences them through visualization, sensation, and touch. The element of Earth evokes an awareness of his belly, and feelings of roundness and contentment. Water feels like a ripple that flows through his whole body, responding to changes in his body and life experience. Air is experienced in his hands as light, soft and caressing, and as reaching out for connection. For Peter, embodied Fire is a passion centered in his heart that radiates outward and is expressed as love of life. Fire is also connected to an experience of sexual energy that radiates downward from his heart. Ether is embodied as a third eye, an infinity sign that connected to consciousness throughout and outside the body.

Further explorations of the Element of Earth give rise to a deepening sense of connection to the core of the Earth, as if engaged in a soft, supportive hug with Mother Earth. A bone dance explores the articulation of the joints as Peter plays with different rhythms and planes of motion. Moving from the organs feels softer, with a rolling, resilient quality that culminates in a warm nurturing embrace of his belly and heart.

Exploring the Element of Water evokes memories of swimming in a tropical sea, as well as being a fetus softly suspended inside the belly of his mother.

*Water*
*Water's smooth and fluid flow*
*Gently ripples through my soul*
*It refreshes, so*
*It replenishes, so*
*It's so soothing*
*The feeling of a bubbling spring*
*Percolating through from head to toe*
*I know my life's blood*
*Is part of me*
*Coming from the primordial sea*
*The fluid flow is still*

Air reminds Peter of the breath of Life and the energy of Chi. In exploring the breath, he finds it sometimes takes him out into space, and his attention drifts. Sounding through his vocal cords allows him to feel the vibration of Air through his body, and he likes how his breath starts out strong and then tapers away to a whisper. He also enjoys expanding his exploration of Air by moving through the space around him, and by using space to interact with others.

*Figure 18*

Although Fire (represented in Figure 18) is embodied in two very different ways for Peter, he feels it is an Element he can really relate to. He loves both the soothing belly warmth as well as the volatile passion of it. Moving with Fire allows Peter to fan the fire in his core so that it radiates out to his arms and legs. The image in the center of the drawing in Figure 18 is a red chili pepper, and represents Peter's love of hot, spicy food as well as a central source of somatic heat and Fire.

Peter especially enjoys experiencing the paradox of the movement exploration of Ether. For him, it means being here but not here, connected but disconnected, moving outside and coming back inside, feeling gravity yet also feeling what it would be like to spin out to the limits. He comments that he would like to continue this exploration on his own, find some music, and start spinning.

*Figure 19*

## Monica

*Monica is a movement teacher who works with people of all ages. She is 39, with an eleven-year-old son. She loves to dance.*

Exploring the Element of Earth raises some intriguing questions for Monica. She experiences Earth as containing all the other Elements, and wonders, if everything is Earth, what does she focus on specifically when she says Earth. She suggests that Earth for her is the matrix, the vessel, the bed where the creative lies down to sprout and take root. The movement explorations involving the skeletal and organs systems elicit different movement qualities - the bone dance has a linear, percussive, shaking quality that traveled through space. Dancing from the organs elicits small, soft, rippling movements that stay contained and connected to the Earth.

Monica likes the Bodypainting activation experiment for the Element of Water, and comes up with ideas for variations to it that include doing the exercise with a few different colors as well as with mud or warm oil. As she expands the Bodypainting into larger movement, she develops an image of swimming at the bottom of the sea and reflects on how the movement exploration could be structured to include that theme. The reflective movement experiment for Water elicits a different quality of flow than the lush body flow of the preceding exercise - this flow has more to do with acceptance and connection.

Embodying the Element of Air through breath allows Monica to find more space and softness, and she begins to relax. Expanding the exploration of her kinesphere into a moving interaction with others, she feels some free creative movements emerge.

Fire is a more difficult Element to access - even after attending to areas in her body where warmth or energy might be stimulated, Monica still feels mostly cold and still. While she is writing about her experience, however, she begins to feel the rumblings of something that might be a volcano.

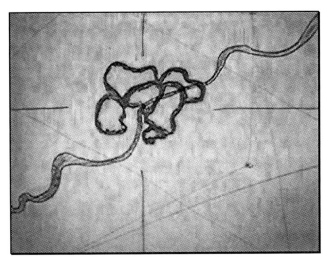

*Figure 20*

The movement exploration for Ether - spinning - is exciting and positive for Monica despite the fact that she feels very afraid to do it. After an initial reluctance, and some dizziness that began before moving, Monica feels elated and expansive while she is actually turning. She is aware of feeling centered and grounded both during and after the movement.

Monica depicts her somatic integration of the Elements in the drawing in Figure 20. In terms of evaluating her experience, she feels as though she has learned more about Ether and has begun to relate the idea of Ether to some of the other somatic experiences she has had. Although she loves Nature, she lives in the city, and does not have the opportunity to be with the Elements as much as she wants. For Monica, being able to explore the Elements within her is a special and valuable skill that she would like to continue.

## Luna

*Luna was born on November 20, 1954, which makes her a Scorpio and a Water sign. She is a graduate of the Ontario College of Art, as well as being a   trained dancer and choreographer. She leads recreational fitness for seniors, creative movement for children and adults, and movement/stress management for people  in recovery from drug addiction. She has recently started teaching yoga.*

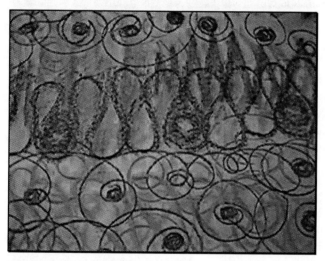

*Figure 21*

Luna's initial exploration of the Elements as they were experienced in her body is met with some internal resistance. When the Elements do come into awareness, they appear very anatomically.  For her, Earth is digging and mudpies; Water is liquid in the eyes and a vessel in the stomach.  Air is experienced as a hollowness in the knees, and Fire as a fever in the ears and head. Ether is embodied as a ladder moving up the spine.

In the movement explorations for Earth, Luna experiences the Earth's connection to body rhythms and expresses it in the drawing in Figure 21 and the following poem:

191

*Ritual percussive*
*release exciting*
*Expressive*
*Energizing*
*Elemental Earth*
*to explosive Fire.*


Exploring the Element of Water creates an experience of peace and tranquillity that results in a release of tension for Luna. She describes feeling as though she were in an aquarium and that the room was completely filled with water and other water beings. As her body floats and is shifted by the water, she loses all sense of time. She finds herself in a timeless ageless ocean as if in the womb. As her breathing slows, she thinks how nice it would be to be able to breathe underwater.

Air evokes similarly relaxing feelings, but with a quality of expansiveness, as if she is much bigger than her body. Luna is aware that she shares the Air with the others in the room, and that "we are all as one". She describes Air as so simple, and yet so vital to our aliveness.

The movement explorations for the Element of Fire are particularly important for Luna. She describes the Fire Dance as extremely healing to the physical pain she has been experiencing over the weekend. The small ember she feels inside her body is like "a miniature sun, the eternal Sun inside the universe inside my body". Finding a safe outlet for her own inner Fire allows her to channel its energy in a positive way. Out of this release emerge feelings of love, humanity, and an awareness of her deep sensitivity to stimuli. On a relational level, Luna feels like sharing her Fire with others, and connects with others in the room who respond to her.

Luna draws the work in Figure 22 in response to the whirling movement explorations of Ether, and describes it as a mysterious energy that connects all life together.

*Figure 22*

In evaluating her experience of Elemental Movement ,
Luna emphasizes the importance for her of being open-minded,
and allowing her own inner process to emerge. She experiences
the Elements as a door to her spirituality and creative process, and
wants to explore Fire and Ether more. She is also interested in
continuing to process her inner experience through meditation and
discussion with others, on both personal and professional levels.

*Figure 23*

## Rae

As primary researcher of this study, and facilitator of the Elemental Movement    program in which the co-researchers participated, my experiences reflect a perspective different than that of those described above. Although I am familiar with all the somatic experiments used in the course of the study, I am still relatively new to the role of observing their effects in others. My creative synthesis of the data is centered on my subjective experience of witnessing the Elements as they were embodied in the movements of my co-researchers.

> *Here comes Earth, so heavy and slow*
> *Breath eases out and bodies sink*
> *Arms and legs expressing such elegant gravity*
> *Safe and certain in its embrace*
>
> *Then Water flows in*
> *And the senses awake*
> *Undercurrents of emotion*
> *Rippling across mouth and brow*
>
> *Air expands everything*
> *Breath and gesture and space*

194

*Shape and volume embodied in motion*
*Inspired by lightness and grace*

*That transforms into passion*
*As bodies catch Fire*
*Intensity radiates from the core*
*Hearts and bellies flicker and blaze*

*Then Ether comes*
*And silence descends*
*Only to emerge in quietly whirling joy*
*Bodies speaking the inexpressible.*

In reviewing and reflecting on my co-researchers experiences, several themes emerge for me in addition to the subjective impressions elicited in witnessing their movements. In both their movements and verbal responses, a sense of connection to Nature was evident. In general, co-researchers' movements were natural and realistic - not forced or affected - and they noticed natural phenomena in the environment around them. A full moon outside the window on the first evening of the workshop was noted by several participants, and the trees and the park across the street were reported sources of pleasurable contact. Many of the co-researchers' writings included mention of Mother Nature or Mother Earth in a way that suggests some experience of the Elements as primal sources of connection was elicited.

The theme of polarities also emerged out the of experiences of co-researchers as they explored the various facets of each Element. Sometimes the polarity was experienced as a difference between two Elements, i.e. Water as soothing and Air as alarming. Other times, the polarity was internal - Fire as both comforting and volatile. Occasionally, the polarity manifested itself as a difference between how people embodied the same Element in visibly contrasting ways. As a witness, I noticed this type of polarized movement on several occasions. For example, in one Water movement improvisation, everyone in the room was engaged in slow undulating movement while lying on the floor - except for one person, who raced through the room as if caught in the current of a roaring river.

195

Another theme that emerged from the Elemental Movement workshop was the *flow* experience. Although co-researchers did not use that term specifically, one of the experiences they described frequently was a whole-body sensation combined with a sense of acting with total involvement. The Element of Ether, in particular, seemed to elicit the flow experience, with its tendency to merge action and awareness, stimulus and response, and self and environment into a unified, connected event.

The use of the Elements as archetypes was also evident throughout the writings and comments of co-researchers. Sometimes these personified projections of the collective unconscious were mentioned by name, such as Mother Earth or the Magician. Other times, there was just a suggestion that the material evoked by Elemental Movement was archetypal in nature. For example, Glenmore's poem of the sailor swimming far out into the Deep, or Iesha's poem in which she describes the Elements as possessing almost human qualities.

Lastly, the use of the Elements as a communication device was frequently evident in the movement of co-researchers throughout the program. Sometimes this non-verbal communication was structured into the experience - for example, when I suggested to the group that they work in pairs for a particular exercise, or that they find a way to make contact with other people in the room as they move. More often, however, these movement interactions occurred spontaneously as individual movers found their movement patterns or qualities responded to by another mover. Sometimes the movement communication was based on a similar response to embodying a particular Element - two people whose movements were similar to one another's might spend a moment consciously echoing and reinforcing those particular movements in each other. Other times, a movement expression of an Element would elicit a movement in response. For example, if someone was expressing Fire by flicking an arm, someone else might "answer" that movement by also flicking an arm. At other times, the movement communication was more complex than a simple "call and response". One mover who lay down during an Air movement improvisation found herself being visited by several other movers over the course of the experiment. They would come over, dance around her in obvious relationship with her, and then depart. Something in the way this woman was embodying the Element of Air seemed to strike a chord in others, and they responded to it by engaging in a brief movement conversation with her.

Many of these movement themes relate back to the principles and concepts described in earlier chapters, and I will make further connections between these concepts and the practice of Elemental Movement    as it manifested in this research study in the final chapter. At this point, however, I would like to share some of the observations co-researchers made about their experiences of Elemental Movement    as a somatic model of movement education, and my reflections on those observations.

## Co-researchers Evaluate the Elemental Movement Model

One of the most interesting questions raised by co-researchers over the course of the program was where this model was located with respect to the continuum between therapy and education.    Although described in the research information package as a model of somatic movement education, it seems clear that the material lends itself equally well to psychotherapeutic applications.  In group discussion and in written comments by co-researchers, it was generally acknowledged that absolute distinctions between what is therapeutic and what is educational cannot usually be made, in theory or in practice.  The same holds true, of course, for the distinction between the psychological and the physical.  Despite this, and despite the fact that Elemental Movement    is a model that emphasizes holistic balance and integration, attending more specifically to the psychological dimensions of the work would probably have been useful for these participants.

As I witness the response to exploring the Elements in this and other settings, I frequently see the initial engagement with the Elements as primarily psychological, rather than kinesthetic.  For example, movers will describe emotionally-oriented responses ("I feel safe and happy") over physically-oriented ones ("I feel a tingling in my chest"). This occurs despite the fact that the explorations in Elemental Movement (and my verbal facilitation of them) are decidedly oriented towards the kinesthetic. This apparent preference for developing an emotional or psychological relationship with the Elements could be explored from a number of viewpoints. A Jungian approach might suggest that because the Elements are archetypes of the psyche, working with them will naturally evoke a decidedly psychological response. A somatic perspective might view the preference for psychological engagement as reflective of a Western cultural bias that tends to exclude or minimize kinesthetic phenomena. Other possible influences include the fact that participants know me to be a psychotherapist as well as a movement educator, and many of them have extensive previous experience in using expressive material psychotherapeutically.

Regardless of the reasons for it, I am not unpleased that Elemental Movement appears to engage people emotionally and psychologically. I have a deep regard for the Elements as psychological archetypes. As a psychotherapist, I recognize the value of emotional and psychological exploration, and want to create the space for that type of work to occur in the context of an Elemental Movement class or workshop. Where my challenge seems to lie is in finding the balance and the connection between the psychological and the kinesthetic, and finding ways to support and facilitate that connection for others. Simply emphasizing the somatic by orienting the material to it does not seem to be enough. By recognizing the strength of the psychological engagement participants are likely to experience in response to the Elements, I can structure the model accordingly. This includes more time to share this material verbally with others, although not necessarily to use it as a starting place for further psychological explorations. I am also interested in developing ways to use the psychological response to the Elements as an avenue for deepening the somatic experience of them.

In terms of overall content and structure, the feedback from co-researchers was generally very positive. There was some variance in feedback in terms of the general tone of the weekend - a few would have enjoyed the opportunity to explore the Elements more deeply and with more intensity, while others voiced their appreciation for the opportunity to work with the Elements in an introductory way that emphasized safety and fun. There were also some useful comments with respect to making transitions between and following Elements. One co-researcher noted that she felt some dizziness after the Air movement improvisation, and suggested that in her previous experience in working with the Elements, that moving into the Air Element before fully exploring her experience of Water tended to evoke this sensation. Another noted that both days of the weekend ended with exploring Elements that tended toward "spaceyness" - Air and Ether. Although there were grounding exercises during the closure section for each day, a change in overall format could probably resolve this problem more effectively.

The organizational format of the workshop received several positive comments. Although time did not permit including an exercise from each of the five steps - Somatic Meditation, Activation, Expressive Improvisation, Interactive Movement Structure, Collective Movement Structure, and Integration - for each of the five Elements, the workshop did follow that same basic structure. Each Element was introduced through a guided somatic exploration that then evolved into movement expression. This was followed by time to process the movement experience through expressive arts explorations and through group discussion before proceeding to the next Element. The expressive arts explorations used in the study were the same or similar to those described in the Expressive Arts Experiments sections in the chapter on Embodied Elements. Feedback about this format indicates that it worked and flowed well, although a wish for more time for movement was also expressed.

Constructive suggestions with respect to more particular aspects of the material were also offered by co-researchers. For example, in the research workshop, I only included *one* Sensory Dimension exploration (as described in the chapter on Embodied Elements), in an effort to streamline the agenda. Feedback from one of the co-researchers suggests that omitting the sensory aspect of the Somatic Meditation for the other four Elements made a difference. In future planning, it might be important to include that component as an integral part of every Somatic Meditation.

Another co-researcher commented how much she enjoyed the Somatic Meditations as a preface to exploring each Element. She found they allowed her to make both physical and mental connections to the Element.

As a facilitator, I have received varying suggestions on pacing and content of the Somatic Meditations. Some prefer few words with lots of time in between verbal suggestions. Others find the space in between too long, and find it hard to maintain their focus on the exploration. Some find that when a facilitator uses highly descriptive language to suggest certain qualities or aspects of somatic experience, they feel less free to create their own details. Still others want more graphic and evocative descriptions to stimulate their imaginations. My goal as a facilitator is to find a balance between these varying preferences, and develop a set of language tools for this work that are uniformly rich, deep, simple, and clear.

Clearly, the auxiliary factors also have an impact on the experience of the model. In this research situation, the environment - both human and physical - seemed to enhance the experience for everyone. Several co-researchers commented positively on the quality of the facilitation, the conduciveness of the space to the work, and the group composition and dynamics. As a facilitator, I feel especially fortunate to have a group of co-researchers who were highly skilled, enthusiastic, and responsive. I am also encouraged by how many co-researchers expressed the strong desire to continue their exploration of the Elements through movement. I feel both challenged and supported to create new movement structures, new processing tools, and additional formats for this work. I am especially interested in offering a class format that would allow participants to explore a single Element at a time, as well as something oriented to those willing and able to work with the Elements at more depth[28]. This would include a deeper investigation of the "shadow" side[29] of the Elements, and

---

[28] The initial context I envision for this type of exploration is recreational/educational rather than clinical/therapeutic. It would be intended for those wishing to pursue Elemental Movement as a form of personal development.

how these more challenging Elemental aspects can be constructively embodied.

There were some additional connections and comments that co-researchers made about Elemental Movement that I would also like to note. One co-researcher was amazed at how different cultures connect to the Elements "no matter what race, gender, sexual orientation, etc." Another commented that they were intrigued by alchemical aspects of this work, and expressed a desire to explore this further through reading. Yet another co-researcher expressed an interest in exploring the connection between the Elemental model used in Elemental Movement and that used in Chinese medicine. They would like to play with cross-references between these different symbol sets. These comments suggest to me that the basic framework of Elemental Movement might successfully be adapted to these more specific investigations. I would be interested to see how it might be used as an alchemical discipline as well as a tool for cross-cultural communication.

## Summary

Returning to the primary research question of this study, the results of the research seem to indicate that the Elements do lend themselves to embodied expression through movement, and that the nature of that expression is both common to humans as somas and singular to the individual. Similar themes are traceable through the individual depictions of embodying a particular Element, such as the *in utero* motif of Water, or the passionate intensity of Fire. At the same time, each individual in this study describes their experience of the Elements in a way that indicates it is clearly unique.

The vividness of the movement expression and the artistic work that emerged out the of the movement suggests that this model is effective in eliciting meaningful and significant somatic

---

[29] Both Jungian and Gestalt frameworks might be employed in this type of work.

material. Further research is needed in exploring the long-term effects of this type of somatic exploration, and how the experience of the Elements is integrated into daily living, and into each individual's sense of somatic identity. As the ancient alchemical writings suggest, the process of differentiating, refining, and integrating the Elements somatically is a task accomplished over a span of years rather than something that is effected over the course of a weekend workshop.

In summarizing the implications of this research study, it is important to consider several factors. Chief among them is the fact that this study was designed as an initial exploration of the Elemental Movement    model, not as a definitive indicator of its specific somatic effects. Further study into the more particular dimensions of this work remains to be done, and may benefit from a more structured research design and the use of quantitative as well as qualitative measures. Another is the relative limitation of the group size and makeup. Ideally, I would like to see additional research done with a larger and more diverse population, as well as more in-depth exploration, perhaps through case studies. Since developing a new model of movement education eventually requires that students of that method learn to replicate for themselves the experiments that test it, at some point it will also be useful to study the effects of a program of Elemental Movement facilitated by someone other than the current researcher.

As a movement educator, the personal and professional ramifications of this research study are very positive. I feel encouraged to continue my work in developing Elemental Movement    , to share the model more widely with colleagues, and to create new applications for the work. It is also my hope that this research study might stimulate others in the fields of alchemy, somatics, expressive arts, movement education, and psychotherapy to recognize their commonalities and the possibilities for integration and cross-fertilization, and to engage in their own exploration of the Elements as tools of personal awareness and development.

# Conclusion

At the beginning of this book, I offered a vignette of a session of Elemental Movement ℠, and described how a particular group of individuals manifested an embodied experience of the Elements. This last chapter contained a far more detailed description of Elemental Movement ℠, as experienced by seven participants in a research study. Sandwiched in between those two descriptions lies a history, a theory, and a guide to practice. What remains is to connect these related components into a cohesive whole, so that the threads of each become interwoven into the larger fabric. Like any somatic model, the most significant and enduring connections to be made about Elemental Movement ℠ are those created by the individual through direct somatic experience. Accordingly, I encourage the reader to experiment with the model, and to discover for themselves how the dimensions of body, mind, movement, and alchemy intersect.

Although everyone's experience of Elemental Movement ℠ will be unique, several threads trace their way throughout this work that I think are essential to understanding how and why the model works. These threads form the warp and woof of the fabric of Elemental Movement ℠, and were introduced in the earlier theoretical sections of the manuscript. I would like to conclude by articulating some of the ways they have emerged in its practice as evidenced by the research data.

One of the fundamental ideas behind the development of Elemental Movement ℠ is that the Elements are collectively-held motifs that embody the essential qualities of human experience. Based on his explorations of alchemy and his study of dreams, Carl Jung postulated the existence of archetypes, and described the Elements as examples of these primal patterns. First described in this manuscript in the section on Inner Alchemy, the significance of the Elements as archetypes becomes clearly apparent in the practice of Elemental Movement ℠. Because archetypes are not just communal but phylogenetic, humans are genetically hardwired to experience the Elements as meaningful and evocative symbols. The implication for the practice of

Elemental Movement   is that the basis of the work is something everyone can relate to, regardless of ontogenetic experience. This idea seems to have been clearly and strongly borne out by the experiences of those participating in the research study - not only did participants immediately respond to the idea of working with the Elements regardless of their previous knowledge or experience with them, the nature and quality of their responses during the study suggests that they were working with material that held the potential for deep and comprehensive inner significance. Each of them approached working with the Elements with a degree of respect bordering on awe, much as I imagine the ancient alchemists might have.

As archetypes, the Elements can be experienced as living and our relationship to them as direct and personal. This primal perspective on the Elements was described in the history of the Elements in relation to aboriginal cultures and pagan spiritual practices, and was also manifested in the experiences of co-researchers during the practice of Elemental Movement   . The human capacity to form relationships with the Elements offers a richness and depth to the experience of working with them as symbols, and adds a relational dimension to the personal territory that can be explored through Elemental Movement   .

Because of their universality, the Elements also possess the capacity to evoke patterns of common experience that create links between members of the human community.   Although appreciating our diversity is essential if people are to form any kind of viable community, identifying with each other through our commonality is often more easily available to us. The Elements offer a conduit for communicating our common experience, and help to strengthen our sense of being meaningfully related to one another.   It is my belief that the positive group dynamic manifested in the Elemental Movement   research study was due, in part, to the kinesthetic empathy created by moving together while sharing a common source of inspiration.

Another important key to understanding the essential characteristics of Elemental Movement   is that the Elements provide resonant symbolic structures for physical, psychological, and spiritual phenomena.  The idea that the Elements work on all these levels was first introduced in the section that described an Ayurvedic understanding of the Elements, and is echoed in the Greek humoural and Western alchemical approaches.  In reporting their experiences of embodying the Elements, co-researchers in the Elemental Movement   research study produced data that also supported the idea that the Elements transcend the arbitrary borders of body/mind/spirit, and allow access to a wide range of human experience.  Not only does the wholistic and integrative capacity of the Elements offer a comprehensive way to address personal change, it also suggests that the Elements would have a natural affinity to mediums of exploration that are also, of themselves, wholistic in nature.

Movement is such a medium, and many of the qualities highlighted here with respect to the Elements are equally true of movement.  Movement is a universal means of communication that allows us to form and express the essential qualities of personal and collective experience.  Like the Elements, movement transcends the boundaries between our physical, psychological, and spiritual dimensions, and direct conscious experience of our movement can foster the wholistic integration of the self.  In the Elemental Movement   research study, co-researchers used movement to access a wide range of personal and interpersonal experiences, and were able to articulate the many facets contained within a single movement experience.

The affinity of the Elements and movement for one other as tools of exploration, expression, and integration is the basis for the development of Elemental Movement  . It is this synergistic merger of the Elements with the medium of movement that uniquely characterizes Elemental Movement   as a model of somatic education.  The materials and ideas outlined in this manuscript represent only the beginnings of an exploration of their intersecting dimensions, and many facets of how this particular symbol set and this particular medium interact remain to be discovered.

# Resources

# Bibliography

A Better Warm-Up. *Allure*. August, 1993, p.58.

Adler, Janet. 1987. Who Is the Witness? A Description of Authentic Movement. *Contact Quarterly*. 1987, 20-29.

Bartinieff, Irmgard. 1980. *Body Movement: Coping with the Environment*. New York, Gordon and Breach.

Becker, Frances. Kinetic Awareness. *Contact Quarterly Dance Journal*. Vol. 18, No.2, Summer/Fall 1993.

Bender, Tom. 1997. *Building with the Breath of Life. The Elements of Energetic Design*. http://users.knsi.com/~tbender/elements.htm. November, 1998.

Benhke, Elizabeth. 1995. Matching. In Johnson, Don Hanlon (ed.). *Bone, Breath, and Gesture*. Berkeley, CA, North Atlantic Books.

Blogg, Martin. 1988. *Healing in the Dance*.

Blom, Lynne Anne and Chaplin, L. Tarin. 1988. *The Moment of Movement: Dance Improvisation*. Pittsburgh, PA., University of Pittsburgh Press.

Brody, Liz. 1996. Move into Bliss. *Shape*. December, 1996.

Calais-Germain, Blandine. 1993. *The Anatomy of Movement*. Seattle, WA, Eastland Press.

Calais-Germain, Blandine. 1996. *The Anatomy of Movement Exercises*. Seattle, WA, Eastland Press.

Chace, Marian. 1964. The Power of Movement with Others. *Dance Magazine*. June, 1987, 42-51.

Chodorow, Joan. 1991. *Dance Therapy and Depth Psychology*. New York, Routledge.

Chopra, Deepak. 1989. *Quantum Healing*. New York, Bantam Books.

Chopra, Deepak. 1993. *Creating Affluence*. San Rafael, CA, New World Library.

Cohen, Bonnie Bainbridge. 1993. *Sensing, Feeling, and Action: The Experiential Anatomy of Body-Mind Centering*. Northampton, MA., Contact Editions.

Cohen, Mark S. *Lecture Notes for Philosophy 320 at University of Washington*. http://weber.u.washington.edu/~smcohen. February, 1999.

Conger, John. 1988. *Jung and Reich: The Body As Shadow.* Berkeley, CA., North Atlantic Books.

Csikszentmihalyi, Mihaly. 1975. Play and Intrinsic Rewards. *Journal of Humanistic Psychology.* Vol.15, No.1 (Winter 1975).

Cummerton, Joan. 1986. A Feminist Perspective on Research. In Nan Van Den Bergh and Lyn Cooper (Editors) *Feminist Visions For Social Work.* Silver Springs, MR, National Association of Social Workers.

*Dance Therapy: Its Research Implications.* 1970. Committee on Research in Dance (CODA).

Davis, Courtney. 1988. The Celtic Art Sourcebook. London, Blanford Press.

Demand, Nancy. *Foundations of Hippocratic Medicine.* http://indiana.edu/~ancmed/foundations.htm. February, 1999.

Gendlin, Eugene T. 1981. *Focusing.* New York, Bantam Books.

Godagama, Shantha. 1997. *The Handbook of Ayurveda.* London, Kyle Cathie.

Green, Marian. 1989. *The Elements of Natural Magic.* Shaftesbury, Dorset, Element Books.

Greene, Debra. 1997. Assumptions of Somatics, Part I. *Somatics.* Spring/Summer 1997.

Greene, Debra. 1997. Assumptions of Somatics, Part II. *Somatics.* Fall/Winter 1997-98.

Greenspan, Stanley. 1997. *Developmentally Based Psychotherapy.* Madison, CT, International Universities Press.

Gustafson, Gail. 1999. *The Influence of Somatic Training on the Performing Arts Community.* Abstract, Ninth Annual Somatics Conference Abstracts of Presentations, Ohio State University.

Haldane, Sean. 1984. *Emotional First Aid.* New York, New Horizon Press.

Hall, Calvin S. 1973. *A Primer of Jungian Psychology.* New York, Penguin Books.

Hall, E.T. 1963. Proxemics: The Study of Man's Spatial Relations. In I, Galdston (ed.) *Man's Image in Medicine and Anthropology: Arden House Conference on Medicine and Anthropology,* 1961. New York, International Universities Press.

Hanna, Thomas. 1970. *Bodies in Revolt: A Primer in Somatic Thinking.* Novato, CA, Freeperson Press.

Hanna, Thomas. 1986-87. What is Somatics? *Somatics*. Part I, Spring/ Summer 1986 pp.4-8; Part II, Autumn/Winter 1986-87, pp. 49-53; Part III, Spring/Summer 1987, pp.57-61.

Haxthausen, Margit and Leman, Rhea. 1987. *Body Sense*. New York, Random House.

Heller, Joseph, and Henkin, William A. 1991. *Bodywise*. Oakland, CA, Wingbow Press.

Herman, Judith Lewis. 1992. *Trauma and Recovery*. New York, Basic Books.

Johnson, Don Hanlon. 1983. *Body*. Boston, Beacon Press.

Johnson, Don Hanlon. 1995. *Bone, Breath, and Gesture*. Berkeley, CA, North Atlantic Books.

Johnson, Don Hanlon. 1997. *Groundworks: Narratives of Embodiment.*. Berkeley, CA, North Atlantic Books.

Johnson, Don Hanlon. 1998. *The Body in Psychotherapy*. Berkeley, CA, North Atlantic Books.

Johnson, Karen and Ferguson, Tom. 1990. *Trusting Ourselves: The Sourcebook on Psychology for Women*. New York, Atlantic Monthly Press.

Juhan, Deane. 1987. *Job's Body*. Barrytown, NY, Station Hill Press.

Juhan, Deane. 1999. Double Binds in the Body Mind. *AHP Perspective*, April/May 1999, pp.18-22.

Jung, Carl G. 1953. *Psychology and Alchemy, 2nd Edition*. Princeton, NJ, Princeton University Press.

Jung, Carl G. 1967. *Alchemical Studies*. Princeton, NJ, Princeton University Press.

Kastner, Mirka. 1996. *Discovering the Body's Wisdom*. New York, Bantam Books.

Kepner, James. 1987. *Body Process*. New York, Gardner Press.

Kestenberg, Judith. 1967. *The Role of Movement Patterns in Development, Volumes I and II*. New York, Dance Notation Bureau Press.

Legge, James. 1994. *I Ching*. Secaucus, NJ, Citadel Press.

Levine, Peter. 1997. *Waking the Tiger*. Berkeley, CA, North Atlantic Books.

Levy, Fran. 1988. *Dance Movement Therapy: A Healing Art*. Reston, VA, American Alliance for Health, Physical Education, Recreation and Dance.

Lewis, Penny. 1981. *Theory and Methods in Dance-Movement Therapy*. Dubuque, IA, Kendall Hunt.

Lewis, Penny. 1986. *Theoretical Approaches in Dance Movement Therapy*. Dubuque, IA, Kendall Hunt.

Lui, Da. 1972. *Tai Chi: A Choreography of Body and Mind*. New York, Harper and Row.

MacLean, Adam. 1999. *Alchemy Virtual Library*. http://www.levity.com. February, 1999.

Marketos, Spiros. 1999. *The Medical School of Cos: Hippocratic Medicine*. http://alpha.mpl.uoa.gr/parko/marketos2.htm. February, 1999.

Mehrabian, A. 1971. *Nonverbal Communication*. Nebraska Symposium on Motivation, XIX, 107-162.

Miller, Jean Baker. 1976. *Toward A New Psychology of Women*. Boston, Beacon Press.

Moore, Thomas. 1992. *Care of the Soul*. New York, HarperCollins.

Murphy, Gardner and Lois B. 1969. *Western Psychology*. New York, Basic Books.

Olsen, Andrea. 1991. *Bodystories: A Guide To Experiential Anatomy*. Barrytown, NY., Station Hill Press.

Parri, Via F. 1999. *Spagyric Notions*. http://www.romagna.com/health/spagyric-notions.htm. March, 1999.

Patterson, M. 1968. *Spatial Factors in Social Interaction*. Human Relations Volume 21, 351-361.

Payne, Helen. 1992. *Dance Movement Therapy: Theory and Practice*. London, Routledge.

Perls, F., Hefferline, R. and Goodman, P. 1980. *Gestalt Therapy, 3rd Ed*. New York, Bantam Books.

Pineault, 1997. *The Basic Stuff of the Universe: Greek Theories of Matter*. http://library.scar.utoronto.ca/ClassicsC42/Pineault/PRES.HTM#element. January, 1999.

Pleasing Shapes. *Allure*. August, 1993, p.58.

Powers, John. 1998. Hollywood's Hit Man. *Vogue*. November 1998. Conde Nast.

Pregadio, Fabrizio. 1996. *A Short Introduction to Chinese Alchemy*. http://www.unive.it/~dsie/pregadio . November, 1998.

Rosner, Jorge. 1987. *Peeling the Onion: Gestalt Therapy and Methodology*. Toronto, Gestalt Institute of Toronto.

Roth, Gabrielle. 1997. *Sweat Your Prayers: Movement as Spiritual Practice*. New York, Putnam.

Roth, Gabrielle. 1998. *Maps to Ecstasy*. Novato, CA, Nataraj Publishing.

Schmais, Claire. 1978. *Dance Therapy: The Psychotherapeutic Use of Movement*. Publisher unknown.

Sommer, R. 1969. *Personal Space*. Englewood Cliffs, NJ, Prentice Hall.

Storr, Anthony. 1983. *The Essential Jung*. Princeton, NJ, Princeton University Press.

Tomm, Winnie (ed.). 1989. *The Effects of Feminist Approaches on Research Methodologies*. Waterloo, ON, Wilfred Laurier University Press.

von Franz, Marie-Louise. 1980. *Alchemy: An Introduction to the Symbolism and the Psychology*. Toronto, Inner City Books.

von Franz, Marie-Louise. 1997. Alchemical Active Imagination. Shambhala.

Waldrop, M. Mitchell. 1992. *Complexity: The Emerging Science at the Edge of Order and Chaos*. New York, Touchstone.

Walker, Barbara. 1986. *The I Ching of the Goddess*. New York, Harper and Row.

Walker, Barbara. 1988. *The Women's Dictionary of Symbols and Sacred Objects*. New York, Harper and Row.

Weiss, Carol H. 1972. *Evaluation Research: Methods of Assessing Program Effectiveness*. Englewood Cliffs, NJ, Prentice-Hall.

Whitehouse, Mary. 1958. *Creative Expression In Physical Movement Is Language Without Words*. Los Angeles, CA, Analytical Psychology Club of Los Angeles.

Whitehouse, Mary. 1958. *The Tao of the Body*. Los Angeles, CA, Analytical Psychology Club of Los Angeles.

Whitehouse, Mary. 1965. *Physical Movement and Personality*. Los Angeles, CA, Analytical Psychology Club of Los Angeles.

Wing, R.L. 1982. *The Illustrated I Ching*. Garden City, NY, Doubleday/Dolphin.

# Videography

*Alchemy: Dreams of Gold.* 1995. Non-Fiction Films. Time/Life Video.

Campbell, Joseph. 1996. *The Spirit Land.* Unapix Entertainment.

*CG Jung: The Wisdom of The Dream.* 1989. Stephen Segalier Films. Public Media Videos.

Highwater, Jamake. 1996. *Primal Mind.* Unapix Entertainment.

# Discography

## Earth
Kronos Quartet. 1992. *Pieces of Africa.* Elektra Nonesuch.
McKennitt, Loreena. 1994. *All Soul's Night.* The Visit, Quinlan Road.
McKennitt, Loreena. 1994. *Between the Shadows.* The Visit, Quinlan Road.
McKennitt, Loreena. 1994. *Marrakesh Night Market.* Mask and Mirror, Quinlan Road.
McKennitt, Loreena. 1997. *Mummer's Dance.* Book of Secrets, Quinlan Road.
Mingus, Charles. *Fables of Faubus.*
Nexus, and Horn, Paul. *African Funeral Song.*
Ogada, Ayub. *Obiero.* Plus From Us.

## Water
Bush, Kate. 1998. *Mna Na Heireann.* Celtic Heartbeat 2, Universal Records.
Cockburn, Bruce. 1976. *Water into Wine.* In the Falling Dark, High Romance Music.
McKennitt, Loreena. 1994. *Bonny Swans.* Mask and Mirror, Quinlan Road.
McKennitt, Loreena. 1994. *Samain Night.* Parallel Dreams, Quinlan Road.
McKennitt, Loreena. 1997. *La Serenissima.* Book of Secrets, Quinlan Road.
McKennitt, Loreena. 1994. *Ancient Pines.* Parallel Dreams, Quinlan Road.
Smetana, Bedrich. *The Moldau.*
Strauss, Johann. *The Blue Danube.*

## Air
Bach, Johann Sebastian. *Brandenburg Concerto No. 5.*
Debussy, Claude. *Dances for Harp and Orchestra.*
Enya. 1991. *Caribbean Blue.* Shepherd Moons, Warner Music.
Stevenson, Savourna. 1996. *Dawn.* Singing the Storm, Cooking Vinyl.
Vaughn Williams, Ralph. *The Lark Ascending.*

## Fire
McKennitt, Loreena. 1994. *Santiago.* Mask and Mirror, Quinlan Road.
McKennitt, Loreena. 1994. *Samain Night.* Parallel Dreams, Quinlan Road.

McKennitt, Loreena. 1994. *Huron Beltane Fire Dance*. Parallel Dreams, Quinlan Road.
McKennitt, Loreena. 1997. *Prologue*. Book of Secrets, Quinlan Road.
McKennitt, Loreena. 1997. *Marco Polo*. Book of Secrets, Quinlan Road.
McKennitt, Loreena. 1994. *Tango to Evora*. The Visit, Quinlan Road.
Whelan, Bill. *Riverdance*.

### Ether
Eno, Brian. *Triennale*. Plus From Us.
McKennitt, Loreena. 1994. *Ancient Pines*. Parallel Dreams, Quinlan Road.
McKennitt, Loreena. 1994. *Full Circle*. Mask and Mirror, Quinlan Road.
McKennitt, Loreena. 1994. *Mystic's Dream*. Mask and Mirror, Quinlan Road.
McKennitt, Loreena. 1997. *Dante's Prayer*. Book of Secrets, Quinlan Road.
McKennitt, Loreena. 1997. *Night Ride Across the Caucasus*. Book of Secrets, Quinlan Road.

## <u>Suggestions for Elemental Ambient Soundtracks</u>
Earth - crickets, wolves, drumming
Water - ocean waves, rainstorm, mountain stream, loons, whales
Air - windstorm, birds, harps, windchimes, flutes
Fire - crackling fire, thunderstorm
Ether - chanting (e.g. Tibetan or Gregorian monks), space-age electronic music


# Internet Resources


Alchemy Virtual Library
*http://www.levity.com*

Alchemy. *Britannica Online*.
*http://www.eb.com*

Arts of Native American Peoples: Dance: GENERAL
CHARACTERISTICS OF AMERICAN INDIAN DANCE: Religious
expression in dance. *Britannica Online*.
   *http://www.eb.com*

Ayurvedic Foundations
   *http://www. ayur.com*

Basic Knowledge of Yin Yang and Pa Kua
   *http://www.covesoft.com/visual_nation/html/basic.html*

Body of Knowledge: Movement Therapy and Education from a Feminist
Somatic Perspective
*http://www.body-of-knowledge.com*

Chemical Elements: Historical development of the concept of element.
*Britannica Online.*
*http://www.eb.com*

Common Ground of European Celts and Indian Vedic Aryans
*http://www.cs.man.ac.uk/~pateld/aryan_dir/vias_home/Celt.html*

Communication: TYPES OF COMMUNICATION. *Britannica Online.*
*http://www.eb.com*

Elemental Astrology
*http://www.ozemail.com.au/~alpha/Astro.html*

John Reid's Course on Practical Alchemy
*http://www.levity.com/alchemy/reid 1-2.htm*

Medicine: THE PRACTICE OF MODERN MEDICINE: Health care and its
delivery: MEDICAL PRACTICE IN DEVELOPING COUNTRIES: India.
*Britannica Online.*
*http://www.eb.com*

Muhammad and the Religion of Islam: ISLAMIC THOUGHT: Islamic
mysticism, Sufism: SUFI THOUGHT AND PRACTICE: Symbolism in
Sufism. *Britannica Online.*
*http://www.eb.com*

Occultism: Alchemy: REGIONAL VARIATIONS: Indian Alchemy.
*Britannica Online.*
*http://www.eb.com*

O'Levy's Translation of Maimonides' Yesodei HaTorah from the Mishneh
Torah
*http://maple.lemoyne.edu/~kagan/YESODEI.HTM*

Rain Dance. *Britannica Online.*
*http://www.eb.com*

Religious Symbolism and Iconography. *Britannica Online.*
*http://www.eb.com*

Siddha Indian Medicine
*http://www.investindia.com/newsite/medicine/siddha.htm*

Taoism - The Mysterious Religion
>    *http://www.etek.chalmers.se/~e7pierre/taoism.htm*

Taoism: History: TAOISM UNDER THE TANG, SUNG, AND LATER
DYNASTIES: Taoism under the Sung and Yuan dynasties.: Alchemical
developments. *Britannica Online.*
>    *http://www.eb.com*

The Development of Human Behaviour: Development in Childhood:
COGNITIVE DEVELOPMENT. *Britanninca Online.*
>    *http://www.eb.com*

The Elements
>    *http://www.astrology.net/astroinfo/introelements.html*

The Four Elements in the Western Tradition
>    *http://key.cyberg8t.com/~hogd/foelmt.html*

The History of Personality Profiling
>    *http://www.axiomsoftware.com/history.html*

The History of Western Philosophy: Ancient Greek and Roman
philosophy: THE PRE-SOCRATIC PHILOSOPHERS: Cosmology and the
metaphysics of matter. *Britannica Online.*
>    *http://www.eb.com*

The Laws of the Basic Principles of the Torah
>    *http://maple.lemoyne.edu/~kagan/YESODEI.html*

The Pentagram and The Elements
>    *http://www.cs.utk.edu/~mclennan/BNA/OM/JO-PE.tx*

The Rotation of the Elements
>    *http://www.cs.utk.edu/%7Emclennan/BA/RE.html*

# Related Professional Resources

International Somatic Movement Education and Therapy
Association (ISMETA)
148 West 23rd Street, #1H
New York, NY  10011
(212) 229-7666

International Expressive Arts Therapy Association
P.O. Box 320152
San Francisco, CA  94132-0152
(415) 522-8959

American Dance Therapy Association
2000 Century Plaza, Suite 108
10632 Little Patuxent Parkway
Columbia, MD  21044-3263

Somatics Journal
1516 Grant Avenue, Suite 212
Novato, CA  94945
(415) 892-0617

# Appendices

## Appendix One

Basic Stretches
*The following muscles and/or muscle groups should be stretched as part of warming up for a session, as well as during the cool-down afterward. Use your favorite stretches, or follow the examples offered by a reputable fitness instructor, either through a class or in a book, magazine, or video.*
- soleus, gastrocnemius, and tibialis anterior
- hamstrings and quadriceps
- lower back and gluteus
- adductors and abductors
- sternoclediomastoid, triceps, biceps, deltoids, and erector spinae
- pectorals, rhomboids, and latissimus dorsi

# Appendix Two

## Application for Review of Human Subjects Research

Name:               Rae Johnson
Division:           Independent Study Degree Program
Mailing Address:    203 Woodmount Avenue
                    Toronto, ON  M4C 3Z7
                    Canada
Funding Source:     none required

Title of Study:     Exploring Elemental Movement
                    as a Somatic Model of Movement
Education
Site of Study:      Toronto, ON  Canada

**Brief Description of Purpose of Study:**

This study is designed to investigate the somatic effects of a somatic model of movement education developed by the researcher. The research questions that form the basis of the study include the following:  " What are the somatic effects of participation in a program of Elemental Movement?" "How does the program affect self-perception of body image?" "How does participation affect kinesthetic perception?" Other questions that will be explored by the research process include, "How do co-researchers relate the Elements as symbols to their experience of their bodies in movement?" "How does Elemental Movement affect use of the kinesphere, range of motion, and use of various of movement qualities?"

**Give details of the procedures which relate to human subjects' participation:**

**A. Is an inducement offered?** No

**B. Age:** Adults ranging from late twenties to early fifties.

**C. Gender:** Female

**D. Other salient characteristics of the subject population:** Co-researchers in the proposed research study are students of professional training in either expressive arts therapy, experiential psychotherapy, or somatic movement therapy.

**E. Number of Subjects:** 8 to 12 persons

**F. Number of times observation will be made:** The observed behavior used in the study will consist of co-researcher and facilitator self-observation recorded at irregular intervals throughout a 12 hour program held over two consecutive days. These self-observations will take the form of drawings, journal notes, and guided discussion. Some of the questions upon which these self-observations will be based include, "What are you aware of experiencing in your body at this moment?" and "How would you describe or express the quality of sensation you are currently experiencing?"

**G. Details of any stresses imposed or likely to be felt:** The study does not involve the deliberate imposition of any stress on co-researchers. It is anticipated that participation in the study will result in an experience of reduced, rather than increased, stress.

**H. How will the following be protected?**

**1. Privacy** Co-researchers will not be asked to reveal anything of a personal nature unless they wish to do so. The submission of any and all self-observations (i.e. journal notes, artwork, etc.) over the course of the program for use as research data will be voluntary.

**2. Anonymity:** Only first names or pseudonyms will be used in the research report.

**3. Confidentiality:** Co-researchers will be instructed not to discuss the identity or experiences of fellow co-researchers without their expressed consent at any time during or following the study. Original copies of raw data generated by program co-researchers will remain in their personal possession. Photographs and photocopies of the raw data designated for use in the research report will be securely stored, and will be accessible only to the researcher. Researcher copies of any data not used in the research report will be destroyed upon final acceptance of the report by the researcher's Independent Study Advisory Committee, probably within three months of completion of the study. There are no plans to recontact research co-researchers once the study is complete.

4. **How will coding be kept separate from obtained information?** This issue is not directly applicable to this research design. It is not anticipated that personally identifying information will appear in the raw data.

I. **Measures to be taken to enable subjects to omit specific procedures or terminate participation:** Guidelines for participation will be communicated to co-researchers both verbally and in writing prior to commencement of the study. These guidelines include the following information: 1) Co-researchers are encouraged to participate in only the activities they choose, 2) Co-researchers are encouraged to adapt procedures or activities to accommodate their own personal preferences, and 3) Co-researchers may withdraw from the study at any time, for any reason, without fear of reproach. If a co-researcher withdraws from the study, any information collected from them will be deleted from the research materials.

J. **Cite your experience with this kind of research:** I have conducted one previous similar research study at the University of Waterloo. The research employed a feminist somatic research methodology and involved the use of a non-equivalent control group pre-test/post-test design in researching the somatic effects of movement therapy on post-traumatic stress.

K. **Briefly describe any testing procedure:** No formal tests or interviews will be conducted in the course of the study. Co-researchers will engage in a two-day program of movement education during which they will record their subjective observations and somatic responses using a variety of arts modalities.

**L.** **Are there any possible risks to the subjects - physical, psychological, or sociological? What procedures will be used to assess and reduce such risks?** The physical stresses of movement education are minimal, and are minimized further by the participation guidelines and by the exercise safety knowledge of the facilitator. The program involves a moderate amount of physical activity, but all guided exercises are designed to be safe, and the risks of physical harm anticipated in the proposed research are no greater than those ordinarily encountered in the performance of routine physical activities. In addition, all co-researchers will be required to complete a Physical Activity Readiness Questionnaire as part of the consent form, in order to screen out those for whom even mild exercise might be medically inadvisable. The anticipated psychological stresses are also low. Although opportunities to encounter, explore and reveal material of a personal nature will arise over the course of the program, the potential risks associated with these types of experience will be minimized. The program structure emphasizes safety in interactions and experiences, and the facilitator is trained to recognize and address potential difficulties before they can detract from a positive experience. Because co-researchers will already have undergone some professional-level training requiring personal exploration, it is not expected that they will encounter unforeseen emotional or psychological difficulty as a result of their participation. Individuals with a serious diagnosed mental illness, or who are currently in emotional or psychological crisis will not knowingly be accepted as research co-researchers. As an additional safeguard, program co-researchers will be required to have access to psychotherapeutic resources during and immediately following the study. No sociological risks are anticipated.

**M. How will subjects' informed consent be obtained?** Please see copy of consent form attached.

**N. Are there any other procedures or details of the study that should be brought to the attention of the Human Subjects Committee?** Co-researchers will be recruited from local training programs and through professional contacts in the psychotherapy, expressive therapy, and movement therapy and education communities. Please see proposed recruitment flyer attached.

**O. Include any questionnaire or interview protocol that you will be using.** Please see copy of Physical Activity Readiness Questionnaire attached.

# Appendix Three

Research Study Co-researcher Information Sheet and Consent Form

| | |
|---|---|
| **Researcher:** | Rae Johnson |
| | Independent Study Degree Program |
| | Lesley College |
| | 29 Everett Street |
| | Cambridge, MA  02138-2790 |
| | |
| | **(416) 467-4673** |
| **Title of Study:** | **Exploring Elemental Movement** |
| | **as a Somatic Model of Movement** |
| **Education** | |
| **Site of Study:** | Toronto, Ontario  Canada |

## Research Goals and Methods

The purpose of this research project is to investigate the somatic effects of an holistic model of movement education developed by the researcher.  The model, called Elemental Movement, integrates somatic theory with philosophical and metaphysical symbolism, and uses the Five Elements of the ancient natural world as a framework for movement exploration and learning.  A more detailed description of the theory and practice of Elemental Movement is included in this information package.

This study will employ a feminist somatic research methodology with a non-experimental program evaluation design.  Co-researchers will engage in a two-day program of movement education in a small (8-12) group format, during which they will record their subjective observations and somatic responses using a variety of arts modalities.  This data will be supplemented by ongoing qualitative phenomenological analysis by program co-researchers in an effort to better understand the relationship between program events and their experience.

## About the Researcher/Program Facilitator

Rae Johnson is a feminist therapist and movement educator in independent practice in Toronto, Canada. A graduate of the Gestalt Institute of Toronto and the University of Waterloo, she has an extensive background in somatic psychotherapy and the expressive arts. She is a Registered Movement Therapist® with the International Somatic Movement Education and Therapy Association, and a Clinical Member of the Ontario Society of Psychotherapists. In over a decade of clinical practice, Rae has developed movement therapy and education programs for a wide range of client populations, including survivors of childhood sexual abuse, autistic children, psychiatric in-patients, and women in recovery from addiction. Rae is also the developer of the Elemental Movement model of somatic movement education which is the focus of this study.

## Potential Risks and Benefits Arising from Participation

The physical stresses of movement education are minimal, and are minimized further by the participation guidelines and by the exercise safety knowledge of the researcher/facilitator. The program involves a moderate amount of physical activity, but all guided exercises are designed to be safe, and the risks of physical harm anticipated in the proposed research are no greater than those ordinarily encountered in the performance of routine physical activities. In addition, all co-researchers will be required to complete a Physical Activity Readiness Questionnaire as part of the consent form, in order to safely screen out those of you for whom even mild exercise might be medically inadvisable. The anticipated psychological stresses are also low. Although opportunities to encounter, explore and reveal material of a personal nature will arise over the course of the program, the potential risks associated with these types of experience will be minimized. The program structure emphasizes safety in interactions and experiences, and the facilitator is trained to recognize and address potential difficulties before they can detract from a positive experience. As an additional safeguard, program co-researchers will be required to have access to psychotherapeutic resources during and immediately following the study.

The potential benefits of participation in the study will vary according to the needs and abilities of each co-researcher. On a physical level, it is hoped that co-researchers will experience an increased awareness of different body systems and movement qualities, as well as an expanded movement repertoire. On a psychological level, co-researchers will have an opportunity to make somatic connections to their experience of creative and emotional expression. It is also hoped that approaching intermodal artistic expression from a somatic perspective will enrich the bodily dimension of their professional knowledge and skills as students of personal growth.


### Time Commitment and Terms of Contact

Participation in this study will involve a time commitment of approximately 14 hours over a three-day period. After a Friday evening meeting to complete an initial Elemental Body Map exercise, a two-day weekend program is followed by a final Body Map and a program evaluation questionnaire. All phases of the study will be conducted in Toronto. There are no plans to recontact co-researchers once the study is complete.


### Selection Criteria and Guidelines for Participation

Selection criteria for the study is intended to be inclusive, and it is hoped that individuals without prior specific training or experience in movement therapy and education will participate. Current or previous training in some form of experiential approach to personal development is a prerequisite, however. Although the goals of the program are educational rather than psychotherapeutic in nature, and anticipated psychological risks of participation are low, program co-researchers are required to have access to psychotherapeutic resources during and immediately following the study.

## Cost of Program and Co-researcher Remuneration

When offered to the public, a movement education program similar to that provided as part of this study would ordinarily cost co-researchers about $200 per person. In consideration of the additional participation required as a result of involvement in the research process, these fees are being waived for study co-researchers.

## Confidentiality

The privacy, confidentiality, and anonymity of research co-researchers will be respected throughout the research process and beyond. Co-researchers will not be asked to reveal anything of a personal nature unless they wish to do so. The submission of any and all self-observations (i.e. journal notes, artwork, etc.) over the course of the program for use as research data will be voluntary.

Only first names or pseudonyms will be used in context of the program and in the research report. All co-researchers will be also be required to agree to not discuss the identity or experiences of fellow co-researchers without their expressed consent at any time during or following the study. The individual experiences of research co-researchers will not be discussed by the researcher with anyone, with the exception of sharing general information about the progress of the study with members of her academic advisory committee. Original copies of raw data generated by program co-researchers will remain in their personal possession. Photographs and photocopies of the raw data designated for use in the research report will be securely stored, and will be accessible only to the researcher. Researcher copies of any data not used in the research report will be destroyed upon final acceptance of the report by the researcher's Independent Study Advisory Committee, probably within three months of completion of the study. There are no plans to recontact research co-researchers once the study is complete.

## Participation in the Study

All guidelines for participation are intended to respect the individual needs and preferences of co-researchers. These guidelines include the following information: 1) Co-researchers are encouraged to participate in *only* the activities they choose, 2) Co-researchers are encouraged to adapt procedures or activities to accommodate their own personal preferences, and 3) Co-researchers may withdraw from the study at any time, for any reason, without fear of reproach. Co-researchers may communicate a decision to withdraw from the study by contacting the researcher, either by phone or in writing. If a co-researcher withdraws from the study, any information collected from them will be deleted from the research materials.


## Consent Form

I agree to participate in the research study conducted by Rae Johnson of the Independent Study program at Lesley College, under the supervision of Drs. John Aram, Julia Byers, and Seymour Kleinman. I have made this decision based on information I have read in the information consent letter, and have had the opportunity to receive any additional details I wanted about the study.

- As a co-researcher in the study, I realize that I will be asked to take part in a two-day program of movement education, complete self-evaluation exercises before and after the program, and record my experiences over the course of the program.

- I have completed the Physical Readiness Questionnaire, and agree to have access to psychotherapeutic resources during and immediately following the study.

- I understand that I may decline to participate in any part of the movement program if I so choose.

- All information which I provide will be held in confidence and I will not be identified by the researcher in the final report.

- I understand that I may withdraw this consent at any time by notifying the researcher of my decision to withdraw from participation in the study.


**Co-researcher's Name:**

**Co-researcher's Signature:**

**Date:**


## Physical Activity Readiness Questionnaire (PAR-Q)

PAR-Q is designed to help you help yourself. Many health benefits are associated with regular exercise, and the completion of PAR-Q is a sensible first step to take if you are planning to increase the amount of physical activity in your life. For most people, physical activity should not pose any problem or hazard. PAR-Q has been designed to identify the small number of adults for whom physical activity might be inappropriate or those who should have medical advice concerning the type of activity most suitable for them.

Common sense is your best guide in answering these few questions. Please read them carefully and answer yes or no to each question.

1. Has your doctor ever said you have heart trouble?

2. Do you frequently have pains in your heart or chest?

3. Do you often feel faint or have spells of severe dizziness?

4. Has a doctor ever said your blood pressure was too high?

5.  Has a doctor ever told you that you have a bone or joint problem that has been or might be made worse with exercise?

6.  Is there a good physical reason not mentioned here why you should not follow an activity program even if you wanted to?

7.  Are you over age 65 and not accustomed to vigorous exercise?

**If you answered yes to any of these questions,** consult with your physician before increasing your physical activity level. Tell her what questions you answered yes to, or show her this copy. After medical evaluation, ask her about your suitability for unrestricted physical activity (probably on a gradually increasing basis), or for restricted or supervised activity to meet your specific needs.

**If you answered no to all of these questions,** you have reasonable assurance of your present suitability for a graduated exercise program. A gradual increase in proper exercise promotes good fitness while minimizing or eliminating discomfort.

## Background Information on the Elemental Movement Program

The somatic model of movement education being investigated in this research study is based on the integration of two different fields of study - somatics and alchemy. Somatics is a term coined by Thomas Hanna to refer to a group of bodywork disciplines sharing a common perspective that privileges the internal subjective experience of the body. In the West, early pioneers of these disciplines shared a concern for the discrepancy they found between the "aliveness" of felt bodily experience and the relative "deadness" of conventional approaches to exercise, dance, and physical manipulation. As they began to question commonly accepted notions of the body and healing, they developed approaches that included and honored what was, for them, the missing dimension of embodiment - **the full experience of the self as a living body.** These new ways of working with the body, begun around the turn of this century in Europe and

America, included the Sensory Awareness work of Elsa Gindler and Charlotte Selver, the German Gymnastik of Mensendieck and Kallmeyer, and the Alexander Technique of Frederick Matthias Alexander. In mid-century America, influences from Eastern holistic practices furthered the evolution of somatics, and the scope of somatic practice was broadened to include Tai Chi, Aikido, and Yoga. Today, many other schools are also widely considered somatic in orientation, such as Feldenkrais Method®, Continuum, Aston Patterning, Rubenfeld Synergy®, Trager®, and Body-Mind Centering.

Alchemy - the model's secondary theoretical base - is the ancient art and science that seeks to understand the essential principles that underlie the form and function of the cosmos, and its symbols are deeply imbedded in the philosophical and religious traditions of many cultures. Alchemy is a multifaceted subject, and can be understood as 1) a proto-chemistry, offering unique approaches to the preparation of medicinal remedies, 2) a source of psychological symbolism, in which the archetypal structure of human thought and feeling is illuminated, 3) an allegorical exploration of the journey of the human soul, and 4) as a newly recognized influence on the world view of important writers, philosophers, and artists throughout history. In this context, alchemy also refers more generally to **the process of changing something ordinary into something special.**

**Elemental Movement is a form of movement education that applies the principles of Somatics and Alchemy as the basis for a process of change.** It involves a process of transforming the *soma,* or the body as experienced from within. It is composed of a series of movement structures - some formal, and some improvisational - that are designed to use movement to access and express the qualities embodied by the five alchemical Elements - Earth, Water, Air, Fire, and Ether. Using the Elements as a framework and as a set of symbolic tools, Elemental Movement employs movement as the primary vehicle for a wide range of personal explorations. On a physical level, the Elements provide a map for exploring different body systems and movement qualities. They are also used as instruments in the development of a high resolution body image and an expanded movement repertoire. On a psychological level, the Elements represent different aspects of the self that can be accessed and expressed through movement. Working with the Elements as archetypes (or primal symbolic patterns of human experience), Elemental Movement echoes the psychological process of individuation through active imagination expressed as movement. The improvisational movement structures also provide an outlet for creative and emotional expression. On a spiritual level, Elemental Movement serves as a form of moving meditation, drawing on the capacity of certain types of ritualized movement to transform ordinary states of consciousness into transcendent experience. Because the Elements have been sacred icons in many religious and spiritual systems, the contemplation of them through movement can also serve a liturgical function.

The rationale that underlies the practice of Elemental Movement is both simple and multifaceted. The basic premise is somatic in its perspective, and proposes that human functioning and experience is enriched through enhanced self-awareness. In turn, increased awareness promotes freedom of behavior through an increase in the range of choices available to us in response to inner needs and the demands of our environment. Therefore, the fundamental objective of Elemental Movement is an increased ability to use oneself fully - to respond effectively, fluidly, and with pleasure to the challenges of being alive.

# Appendix Four

<u>**Participant Bio Request**</u>
Name:
Pseudonym for Purposes of Research Report:
How You Would Like To Be Described for Purposes of Research Report:
(Please include only the information that feels important to you.)

<u>**Evaluating Your Experience**</u>
*The following questions are designed as a guide to help elicit some of the aspects of your experience with Elemental Movement , in order to enhance a sense of integration and closure. Please feel free to add to these questions, or to modify them to reflect your own needs.*

What am I taking away with me from this experience? What have I learned or gained from it?

What unmet expectations or hopes am I leaving with? What do I still want or need to learn?

What is unfinished about my own process of exploring the Elements?

Where do I go next in my exploration?

<u>**Evaluating the Elemental Movement Model**</u>

*The following questions are designed as a guide to help elicit some of the aspects of your experience with respect to how the model of Elemental Movement presented in this study worked (or didn't work) for you. Please feel free to add to these questions, or to modify them to reflect your own needs.*

What worked for me about this model in terms of how effective it was in enhancing my experience of how I embody the Elements? What didn't work?

What would I have added to the experience? What might I have left out?

How did the auxiliary components of the program (i.e. the environment, the facilitation, the group members) affect my experience of the program itself?

CPSIA information can be obtained
at www.ICGtesting.com
Printed in the USA
FSOW01n0938050617
35025FS

9 781581 121322